'THE FARMER FE..

A Short History of Shropshire Agriculture

by

PAUL STAMPER

Paul Stamper

9 April 1991.

SHROPSHIRE BOOKS

Shropshire V.C.H. Booklet no. 3

Previous titles in series

1   Shropshire and its Rulers: a Thousand Years (1979)

2   Monastic Shropshire (1982; reprinted 1988, 1989)

FRONT COVER: *Cattle at Buildwas Abbey, 1841.*
BACK COVER: *Harvesting oats at Bwlchydonge, on the Welsh Border five miles west of Oswestry.*

ISBN: 0 903802 43 0
Published by Shropshire Books, Shropshire Leisure Services, Preston Street, Shrewsbury © 1989
Cover and book design: Sarah Barker
Typeset by K.C. Graphics Ltd., Shrewsbury
Printed in Great Britain by Midland Printing Services, Shrewsbury

Contents

Foreword

by the Agricultural Story Editor of 'The Archers'

Farming is changing, but there is nothing new in that. It has been developing and adapting to shifting circumstances for thousands of years, as this fascinating book amply demonstrates. All knowledge, we are assured, is a product of history and there has never been a time when it has been more important to determine the future by resolving the apparently conflicting interests of agricultural advance and 'green issues'.

In spite of the technological revolution of the last forty years, which has brought more change to our farms than any similar period in the past, the basic laws of agriculture remain reassuringly untouched. The plant breeders and agro-chemical firms may have made possible a doubling of yields since the last war, but seedtime and harvest still hold sway. The gestation period of the highest yielding modern Friesian is just as long as that of Lord Hill's improved Shorthorns over a century ago. And cows still need milking seven days a week. Bad weather affects a farmer's bank balance more than the machinations of Brussels. The flail gave way to the thresher which in turn yielded to the combine harvester – but no ingenious food processor, no brilliant biotechnologist, has yet managed to create a grain of wheat. It remains undeniably true that 'the farmer feeds us all'.

This book sets the recent past in the perspective of five thousand years of agricultural progress, all the more convincing by relating it to places we know. Shropshire Books, the University of London, and the author are to be congratulated on its timely appearance.

Anthony Parkin

List of Illustrations

Preface

This booklet is condensed from *Agriculture*, volume IV of the *Victoria History of Shropshire* (1989), written by a team of contributors comprising Mr. G. C. Baugh (also the volume's editor), Dr. P. R. Edwards, Mr. R. C. Hill, Miss A. J. Kettle, Dr. R. Perren, Mr. R. T. Rowley, and Dr. P. A. Stamper. In that volume fuller treatment will be found of themes necessarily touched upon but briefly here, and also notes on the authors' sources .– information vital to the inquiring reader.

The figures were drawn by Mr. K. J. Wass and the author. Photographic prints were produced by Mr. S. Pike, Mr. S. Ryal and Mr. V. Williams.

The booklet's title is drawn from a dialogue of a thousand years ago imagined by Aelfric, a leading Anglo-Saxon churchman and writer, in his *Colloquy*. His book was designed to help young scholars to speak Latin correctly, and contains descriptions of the daily lives of men of different occupations.

Master: 'Which secular occupation is the most important?'

Pupil: 'Agriculture, because the farmer feeds us all'.

EARLY TIMES

The first farmers

Farming, the growing of crops and the management of domesticated animals, came to this country from mainland Europe between a quarter and a half million years ago. Before that, since he first arrived in north-west Europe about a million years ago, man had lived by hunting and by gathering wild plants, fruits and nuts. Shropshire was then densely wooded, with dank, wet alder carr and willow wood in the river valleys and on the flood-plains and mixed broadleaf woods, in which lime was probably the predominant species, on the higher, drier ground.

The development of agriculture led to such momentous changes that it is called the Neolithic (or 'new stone age') revolution. People began to live in permanent settlements, to lay out fields, and to develop the equipment necessary for farming such as axes, querns, sickles, and pottery containers. In the 1,500 or so years that the Neolithic period lasted in Britain society became complex and apparently highly organized. Massive projects were undertaken such as the construction of communal tombs, and ceremonial or religious centres like Stonehenge.

The Shropshire area, however, remained sparsely populated and heavily wooded, and clearances for agriculture, as at Bromfield and at Sharpstones Hill near Shrewsbury, were small and short lived. It was probably only around 2,600 B.C., at the end of the Neolithic period, or at the start of the ensuing Bronze Age, that agriculturists moved into the area in any numbers. New farming techniques were then developing, notably transhumance, whereby herds were moved in summer to upland grazing away from the herdsmens' homes and winter pastures in the lowlands. Just across Shropshire's western border at Trelystan on the Long Mountain, the excavator of one of the four hill-top barrow groups suggested that the hill provided summer grazing for the herds of the barrow builders, whose settlements lay down on the lower land. In Shropshire itself the numerous round barrows on the uplands of the south and west of the county, such as the Long Mynd, and also traces of possible Bronze Age 'Celtic fields', indicate that there too the uplands were farmed. Moreover, pollen preserved in Shropshire peat bogs shows that it was in the Bronze Age that the first permanent clearances were made into the broadleaf woods on the

1

lower lands, although generally vast tracts of woodland remained, especially on the wetter, heavier, soils.

In the late Bronze Age, the late 2nd and early 1st millenium B.C., major changes began to affect society. The climate deteriorated, some upland areas ceased to be farmed, and there are signs that competition for resources was becoming violent. Ordinary settlements began to be equipped with defences and about 800 B.C. hillforts, defended hill-top villages, appeared, Shropshire's uplands having one of the densest concentrations in Britain.

CAER-DIN RING, CLUN
A ditched hill-top enclosure of about two hectares. It was probably constructed in the Bronze Age or Iron Age for corralling grazing stock, which would be funnelled towards the entrance on the left-hand side of the enclosure by the approaching ditches.

Soon after hillforts began to be built iron began to be exploited, this marking the start of the period known traditionally as the Iron Age. In a way that bronze had never been, iron was soon in common use, even for basic farm tools, and the new tools enabled agricultural tasks to be performed more quickly and more land to be worked. The pollen evidence shows that in the Shropshire area there were large-scale felling campaigns in the Iron Age, first of broadleaf woods and then of the alder and willow woods in the river valleys. As trees were cleared and ploughing began soil erosion started, and scientists have found that massive amounts of eroded soil which had been washed into the river were deposited as alluvium by the Severn during the Iron Age.

Although details remain sketchy it seems that in the Iron Age there was a considerable difference between the upland farming landscape and the lowland one. The uplands, dominated by the hillforts, were mainly open pasture, with perhaps just a few main boundaries dividing one group's grazing land from another's. By contrast, much of the lowlands, especially the better drained soils along the Severn and its tributaries, was taken up with hundreds of single, family-run farms, each surrounded by its own fields and closes. The farm buildings would usually include a round dwelling house, where tasks such as weaving might also go on; a grain store, raised on four large corner posts; and sheds or pens for animals. All the buildings lay within a substantial enclosure formed by a ditch 2 or 3 metres deep, with an internal bank topped by a palisade or hedge. Although wolves and other wild animals still roamed the countryside, it seems likelier that the defences were raised against raiders and rustlers.

Romans and Saxons

The army of the Emperor Claudius invaded southern Britain in A.D. 43, and within five years the Roman legions were pushing into western England. Forts were established at Wroxeter and elsewhere, although it was only twelve years later that the area was fully subjugated as the Romans thrust into Wales to destroy one of the main centres of resistance, the Druid priesthood on Anglesey. Superficially the changes that took place in the Shropshire area under the Romans were considerable. The hillforts were either taken by force in the conquest or peacefully depopulated soon after, new roads such as the Watling Street (the modern A5) were laid out, and towns were established: one of the country's largest at *Viroconium Cornoviorum* (Wroxeter) and a much smaller one at *Mediolanum* (Whitchurch). One of *Viroconium's* recent excavators has suggested that it may have served, as Oswestry and, much later, Craven Arms were to do, as one

AN IRON AGE OR ROMANO-BRITISH FARM
Showing as dark lines in the ploughsoil, close to Lodge Farm, Quatt Malvern. The area of the two main enclosures (left of photo), one perhaps occupied by farm buildings and the other a paddock, is similar to that of the nearby Victorian farm.

of the main funnels for the cattle trade between what are now Wales and England. Clearly much effort went into cattle breeding, and bones from *Viroconium* show how imported stock was used in the 1st and 2nd centuries to improve the native cattle. Better sheep breeds too were introduced, although, at least in terms of the amount of meat eaten, in *Viroconium* neither mutton nor pork was ever as popular as beef. Of the cereals that came into the town wheat was commoner than barley, while oats and rye were rare. Evidence has also been found at *Viroconium* of the consumption of peas, blackberries, elderberries, and hazel nuts.

Under the veneer of Romanization, however, life in the countryside seems to have continued little changed. Fewer than ten simple Roman-style villas are known in rural Shropshire; they presumably replaced round houses that the owners considered rustic and old fashioned. For most farmers the only difference was that taxes were paid to a representative of Rome rather than of the local tribal chief.

Likewise the departure of the legions in the early 5th century probably had little effect on the area's farmers. Politically the area eventually came under Saxon rule, but any immigration was small-scale and took place at least 200 years after the initial settlement in eastern England. Nevertheless major changes in how land was farmed occurred from the 5th to the 10th centuries. Farmhouses, formerly scattered across the landscape, began to be grouped into villages and hamlets. In these new settlements farmers did not hold their land as separate fields but as a number of long thin strips of land in large open fields, sometimes called 'common' fields because after the crop had been cut all the villagers, or commoners, had the right to put their animals into them to graze on the stubble and weeds.

The emergence of villages and open fields is one of the cardinal changes in English history, which fundamentally determined how people lived in the countryside and how land was farmed for a thousand years. We remain ignorant, however, of what led to that change, and historians remain deeply divided about whether local landlords, whose influence grew much stronger in the late Saxon period, or the villagers themselves were responsible for such radical reordering of the countryside. Most agree, however, that the underlying cause was a rising population and an ever increasing pressure on land.

THE MIDDLE AGES

The Domesday landscape

In 1066 Duke William of Normandy's forces landed in Sussex, and rapidly seized control of the kingdom. Shropshire's farmers would soon have been aware of the new order: Norman lords replaced Saxon ones, castles were thrown up, and in due course the new lords began to build or rebuild their churches in the fashionable Romanesque, or 'Norman', style. But the Normans introduced no agricultural innovations, and in the Shropshire countryside the annual farming round continued as before.

In 1085 King William determined on a survey of his new realm. As with almost every government survey thereafter people resented the intrusion into their lives and were suspicious of the motives behind it. One Saxon grumbled that so thoroughly was the inquiry made that there was 'not even one ox, nor one cow, nor one pig which escaped notice.' The same sentiment is reflected in the name which soon became attached to the survey – Domesday Book, because it seemed that therein was all the information needed for the Last Judgement. Although, sadly, some information collected was omitted from the fair copy of Domesday Book – in Shropshire livestock numbers were left out – it remains a unique record of the 11th-century countryside. Everyone then lived on a manor. Variations occur, but essentially a manor comprised the lord's house, his farm, and the houses and lands of the manor's peasants who held their property in return for work on the lord's land. In Shropshire there was usually just one manor in each village, although in a number of cases, as at Clungunford, a village and its lands were split between two or more different lords, and hence manors.

Peasants were divided into several classes according to their legal status and the kind of land they held. Most numerous were villeins, who held a house and a share of the manor's land and grazing rights in return for their work on the lord's farm. There were also 'bordars', who were probably smallholders, 'oxmen' who looked after and drove the lord's ploughteams, and *servi*, or slaves. Sometimes social classification was abandoned, and instead Domesday's compilers noted people by their occupation, such as priest, miller, smith, or beekeeper.

When it came to recording how much land was farmed the emphasis was on arable land and woodland; grassland was largely ignored. Arable was documented in terms of how many ploughs it took to work it; at Stokesay, a large and prosperous manor, five ploughs worked the lord's land and another eight were shared by 20 villeins. More typical were places like Preston upon the Weald Moors with two ploughs and Aston Botterell with three. Woods were recorded either in terms of their length (and sometimes breadth as well) or according to how many pigs could feed in them in autumn on acorns and beech nuts.

When all Domesday Book's statistics are put together a fairly clear picture emerges of what was going on in different parts of the county. The most valuable estates lay east and west of Shrewsbury and in Corve Dale. These were relatively populous areas, with good, well-drained soils and large areas of arable land, yet still retaining extensive tracts of valuable woodland. The Clun area was only lightly populated and had little arable land yet its estates were quite highly valued, probably an early reflection of the importance of the wool trade. Of the remainder of the county the south-east enjoyed average population and prosperity, while the northern third was relatively poor and undeveloped, especially the border area, recently the scene of much raiding and military campaigning.

Domesday Book, however, was a rare and precocious foray into record making. More than a century was to pass before even such a great landowner as the bishop of Winchester began to require a written record of income, sales, and yields from his estates, and it was only in the mid 13th century that lesser lords began to do the same. Because of that increase in written records, a mass of detail becomes available from *c.* 1250, and many aspects of farming suddenly come into sharp focus.

Villages, fields, and peasants

The rural landscape in the later 13th century was busy and full. People lived in villages or hamlets surrrounded by arable land whose main crops were cereals. Much of that land was divided into strips or 'selions', usually about 8 yards wide and perhaps 200 long. Every farmer in the village held most, if not all, his land as strips; the lord of the manor might have between 50 and 100, the ordinary peasant 10 to 20, and the poor peasant only a few. Each man's strips lay scattered throughout the settlement's arable land, presumably to ensure that everyone had a share of land that was good and bad, wet and dry, near the settlement and far away, and so on. Every year a third of the settlement's land was left fallow, or uncultivated, to allow fertility to return to the soil. Of the cultivated land part would be used for autumn-sown crops and part for spring sown ones. To allow this three-course rotation settlements' arable lands were divided into three 'seasons'. Sometimes all the arable lay in three large open fields. Especially where the terrain was irregular or heavily wooded, however, a settlement's arable land might also lie partly in scattered hedged or walled closes. Closes too were divided into strips held by different men, and each was alloted to one of the settlement's 'seasons'.

Medieval farmers understood the need to retain soil fertility. When land was left fallow animals would be grazed on the stubble and weeds, depositing dung directly where it was needed. Later the fallow might be

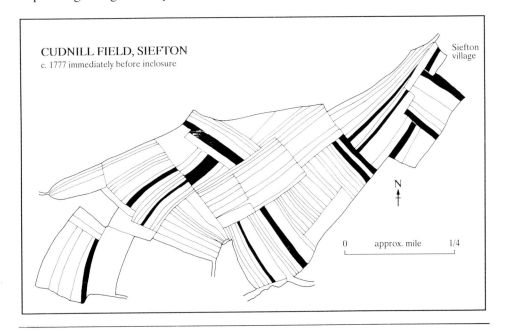

CUDNILL FIELD, SIEFTON
c. 1777 immediately before inclosure

Siefton village

N

0   approx. mile   1/4

CUDNILL FIELD, SIEFTON
At Siefton the medieval open fields survived until the 1770s. Cudnill field lay south-west of Siefton village. The shaded strips are those of one farmer, Morrice Langford.

ploughed in an attempt to reduce weed infestation. Manure from stockyards and byres would be spread before ploughing. Marl, a type of subsoil, was increasingly put on fields in the 13th century to improve soil texture. Many documents mention the local pits where marl was dug; they were clearly dangerous and unpleasant to work in, and undercuts frequently collapsed, crushing or drowning the diggers. Lime was probably little used.

Cereals can be divided into those sown in the autumn ('winter corns') and those sown in the spring. The former comprised wheat, the chief bread corn, and rye, occasionally used alone to make a dark and heavy bread but more often mixed with other grains. The spring corns were barley, used mainly as malt in brewing but also for bread and fodder, and oats, used to feed horses and as a porridge. Records show that oats was the commonest cereal grown in Shropshire in the Middle Ages, while wheat was the main winter corn, sometimes grown mixed with rye. Little barley was cultivated; usually it was grown mixed with oats as 'dredge'. Seed corn was usually kept back from the previous harvest, although wheat seed especially might be bought, usually from dealers at Shrewsbury. Yields were extremely low: wheat at Adderley between 1322 and 1324 yielded just over 3:1 and oats 2:1, while at Cleobury Barnes in 1377-8 the figures were 5:1 and just over 2:1. Margins were thus so slim that one poor crop could prove disastrous. Small quantities of peas, beans, and vetch were also sown in spring in the open fields as well as in crofts and gardens. Some peas were eaten fresh but usually pulses were harvested when dry using sickles or hooks, the dried peas and beans later being separated out by threshing and sieving. Leeks, onions, garlic, cabbages, turnips, herbs, flax, and hemp were also cultivated in gardens. Fruit such as apples and pears was grown, and orchards adjoined most manor houses.

All grain had to be ground at the lord's mill. Watermills began to be built in the Saxon period, and by 1086 there were at least 98 in Shropshire. Most manors had at least one by 1300. Relatively little is known about their technology and appearance, and one of the few detailed references tells how the miller at Hope Bagot fell between the mill's two waterwheels and was crushed to death in 1292. Windmills were being built in England by the 1180s but did not reach Shropshire until the mid 13th century. They later spread all over the county, but were never as common as watermills.

Ploughing was the main task each year in the agricultural round. The plough cut and turned a single furrow, and the ploughman did well to manage an acre a day. In Shropshire lords used eight-ox ploughteams by

POST-MILL NEAR PRESTON BROCKHURST
As shown on a map of about 1740, this mill stood on high ground in Besford wood, north-east of Preston Brockhurst. It would have been quite familiar to a medieval miller. The body of the mill, perched on massive timber supports, could be pivotted to take full advantage of the wind, whose direction is indicated by the flag.

preference throughout the Middle Ages. Oxen were male animals that had been castrated. This rendered them docile, while hormonal changes caused the long bones to continue to grow, giving a taller, less squat animal than the bull. In general medieval cattle were much smaller than modern animals, and stood only about 1.10 m. high to their withers. Documents mention black, brown, red, and grey oxen and hint at the variety of types found. Oxen were expensive to buy and keep, and only the lords of manors and the wealthiest peasants possessed a full team. Most peasants owned one or two oxen, and then combined with their neighbours to put together a team of four or more animals. Some – smallholders or those living in small and impoverished hamlets – might struggle along with a team containing cows, heifers, or even a donkey. After ploughing the land was harrowed, to break it up and level it, and to bury any seed that had been sown. To pull the harrow, a heavy timber frame with iron teeth set in it, a stocky horse or 'affer' was used.

Arable farming was labour intensive, as it was to remain until the 20th century. First there was the slow business of ox ploughing, which would spread over the whole time between perhaps September and March. When the land was ready the seed had to be sown broadcast by hand (a highly skilled job), and perhaps peas and beans set in individual dib holes.

THREE OF THE LABOURS OF THE MONTHS
Early 15th-century glass roundels from Lower Pulley Farm, near Bayston Hill. Each is about 165 mm. in diameter and formed part of a series of twelve scenes.
Top left *June: a man uses a weedhook and crotch to weed between rows of corn.*
Top right *August: the corn is cut with a sickle.*
Bottom left *September: a flail is used to thresh the corn, tied up in sheaves.*

Harrowing might both precede and follow sowing. Hand weeding would later be necessary to keep down the weeds, but it was frequently neglected. The key summer job before the corn harvest was haymaking, when meadow grass was cut, turned, and dried, and then gathered in to form winter feed. Corn was also left to dry in the field after cutting, tied in sheaves: when fully dry they were carried to the farm, ready to have the corn separated from the

11

husks and chaff by threshing, beating with a flail, followed by winnowing, blowing the debris off the corn by throwing it up inside the barn into a draught created either by having the barn doors open or artificially with a winnowing fan. Threshing and winnowing were long and tedious jobs, but could be fitted into periods during the autumn and winter when the weather was bad or there was little else to do.

Most lords employed some full-time farm workers, paid in carefully graded amounts of cash and food according to their job. If the estate was large and comprised several farms, a bailiff or reeve would act as the lord's agent, checking that work was done properly and undertaking the purchase and sale of goods and produce. Other full-time employees might include ploughmen, shepherds, swineherds, dairymaids, and carters. Otherwise the demesne, as the lord's land was called, was farmed using seasonal labour. Until about 1300 much of that came in the form of the labour services owed by the manor's villeins in return for their holdings. How much work villeins owed varied widely from place to place. In Condover in the 1260s each peasant had to work four days a week on the demesne and also do an extra four days' ploughing and harrowing at some stage when needed. Those services, however, were exceptionally heavy for Shropshire and more typical were those at Wattlesborough, where every tenant of a standard holding owed each year three days' ploughing, a day's reaping, and a day's weeding. Such services were naturally unpopular with the peasants. It was perhaps heavy labour services that peasants at Wenlock were complaining about in 1163 when they 'threw down their ploughshares' and refused to till the priory's land. Neither were labour services efficient, for unless carefully supervised the peasants were unlikely to put much effort into the work. Thus in the 13th century lords began to commute labour services, that is accept cash from the peasant in lieu of his work, and most services had been commuted by 1400. The services which survived longest, in some cases long after 1400, were the haymaking and harvest ones; by retaining those lords made sure they had labour on call to get in the hay and corn. In the place of peasants doing labour services lords employed more wage labourers, paid yearly, daily, or on a piece-work basis. In 14th-century Shropshire women and migrant Welsh workers made up a large part of many harvest gangs.

On larger manors the farm buildings were grouped around one or more yards. At High Ercall in 1424 a large farmyard adjoined the manor house with two barns, three stables, ox and cow houses, a dovecot, and stores for grain and hay. There was a similar, but slightly smaller complex at

Chelmarsh in the 1450s, comprising the manor house and its outbuildings, two stables, a barn, ox and cow houses, and a dovecot. Smaller farms might comprise just a house, barn, and animal pens.

Pastoral farming

It was only in a few parts of the county that arable farming predominated. Although large amounts of new land were brought into cultivation in the Middle Ages, much woodland still survived, while in the uplands of the south and west of the county, and on the moors and heaths of its northern third, wide areas of unimproved grassland or scrub remained untilled.

The commonest animal kept in Shropshire in the early Middle Ages was the sheep. For peasants with just a few animals the main attraction was the sheep's milk, used to make cheese, whereas for those with larger flocks wool production was paramount. Mutton was not produced for its own sake. It seems likely that sheep farming was already important in Shropshire in the early Middle Ages. By the 13th and 14th centuries Shropshire's wool merchants were among the country's greatest, carrying large cargoes of high quality wool to European cloth manufacturers. Shrewsbury, for instance, was the base of the Ludlows, one of whom, Lawrence, the builder of Stokesay castle, was drowned in the English Channel in 1294 when crossing with a cargo of wool. The Prides too lived and traded in Shrewsbury; Pride Hill is named after them.

One of Shropshire's leading sheep farmers in the 14th and 15th centuries was the earl of Arundel, who owned extensive estates around Oswestry and Clun. In 1349 he had over 3,000 sheep in the Clun area and almost 1,000 on his Oswestry lands. Other big wool producers included Wenlock priory and Shrewsbury abbey, 847 of the latter's sheep being washed and sheared in 1333. In fact wherever there was sufficient grazing – and in Shropshire that was almost everywhere – lords kept a flock of at least 100 or 200 animals.

The earl of Arundel's flocks were each about 240 strong, and each was in the care of one shepherd although additional help was needed to milk, wash, and shear the sheep. Flocks were pastured on hills, heaths, and other commons and on arable land when it lay fallow; 'red stone' was used to make identifying marks on the sheep and bells were hung around their necks to enable the shepherd to keep track of them. In the winter additional feed was supplied in the form of hay and sometimes peas and vetches, and oats for milking ewes and bran for lambs. Fern or pea straw litter provided bedding at lambing time. Tallow and oil were used to waterproof the sheep, tarpitch and verdigris to treat cuts, sheep scab and foot rot, and various kinds of ointment to treat other ailments. Despite this care sheep remained far more prone to disease than other stock. In bad years losses could be devastating, as at Dodington in 1341-2 where 146 of the 169 ewes in the lord's flock died. Even when averaged out the mortality rate from disease was high by modern standards; at Ruyton in the 14th century it was about 14 per cent.

By the late 13th century some peasants too had large flocks, and a Callaughton man had 70 sheep stolen in 1274. That trend, of emerging specialist sheep farmers, became more marked in the 14th and 15th centuries, and in Morfe forest, near Bridgnorth, average flock size seems to have grown from 13 in 1362 to almost 100 in 1497. In the upland, wooded, and often marginal areas of south Shropshire goats seem to have been important to the early medieval peasants. Goats have a remarkable ability to convert underwood and rough and moorland grazing into milk and meat,

MISERICORD IN ST. LAURENCE'S CHURCH, LUDLOW
This elaborately carved bracket beneath a turn-up seat in the choir, shows a winter scene in a well-to-do 15th-century household. A man warms himself before a fire, which heats a bronze vessel containing drink. Behind him hang two flitches of bacon.

and they can be kept on terrain unsuitable for sheep. In 1255 goats were kept on Stretton's hills, and were said to be the sole means of livelihood for Stretton's poor. As late as 1280 some goat herds in south-west Shropshire were sizeable, even 50 strong. Nevertheless by then goats were increasingly excluded from woods and commons because of the damage they did to the vegetation, and thereafter it was more and more unusual for people to own more than one or two goats.

After sheep, pigs were the commonest animals kept in medieval Shropshire. They were not the fat, white, sty-bound porkers of modern times but much smaller, thin legged, and often dark skinned or black animals. They fed by grubbing and rooting, usually in woods, and between mid September and mid November, the 'mast' months, they grew fat on acorns and beech nuts ready for slaughter. Lords owned fewer pigs than sheep, and the 60-strong herd owned by the lord of Stokesay in 1395-6 was larger than most. By contrast, especially in well wooded areas, peasants tended to keep more pigs than sheep and herds of between 10 and 20 animals were common. In Little Wenlock's woods 23 tenants had at least 200 swine between them in 1397, and in large woods, like that belonging to Wem in 1290, or Morfe forest in 1497, over 1,000 pigs belonging to 100 or more people might be feeding at any one time.

Pig, sheep, and, in the early Middle Ages, goat husbandry were the main branches of pastoral farming. Peasants rarely had more than one or two cows, and even on the biggest estates herds were small, and especially in the early Middle Ages devoted mainly to the production of oxen rather than beef or dairy products. Milk and cheese tended to go for home consumption rather than to market, and in 1538 Lilleshall abbey had 40 cheeses in its dairy house. Young beef was a luxury enjoyed only by the wealthy, and if ordinary people ever ate beef it was from oxen or cows that were too old, sick, or weak to work.

Workhorses, like oxen, were bred by peasants as well as lords, and in certain areas where there were sufficient commons, such as Shrawardine and Halesowen, horse breeding may have formed a significant part of the peasant economy. Better animals, however, were required by lords, wealthy churchmen, merchants, and the like as riding horses, and best quality bloodstock was needed to produce the heavy warhorses or 'destriers' ridden by knights. To that end several aristocratic households kept studs in the Welsh marches. Within 30 years of the Norman Conquest Robert de Bellême, earl of Shrewsbury, was developing his marcher studs. Gerald of

Wales, who visited Shropshire and the adjoining Welsh lands in 1188, reckoned it was the Spanish bloodstock imported by Earl Robert that made the region's horses 'high bred to look at, . . . full limbed, . . . of good size, whilst in speed they are unsurpassed'. Later the earl of Arundel had important studs at Bromhurst park (near Oswestry) and at Clun, the Mortimers had one at Earnwood, and the lords of Caus one in Minsterley

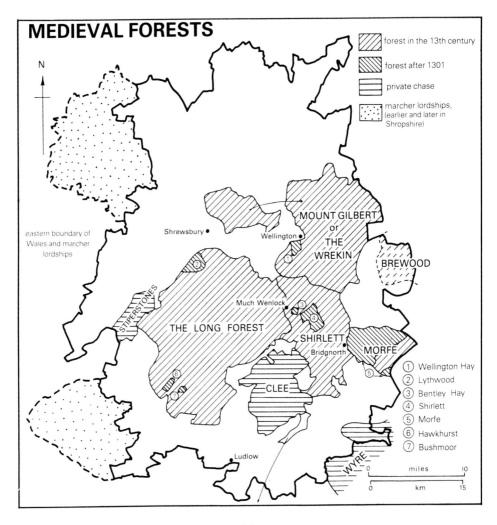

MEDIEVAL FORESTS

N

forest in the 13th century

forest after 1301

private chase

marcher lordships,
(earlier and later in
Shropshire)

eastern boundary of
Wales and marcher
lordships

Shrewsbury ●

Wellington ●

MOUNT GILBERT
or
THE
WREKIN

BREWOOD

STIPERSTONES

Much Wenlock

THE LONG FOREST

SHIRLETT

Bridgnorth ●

MORFE

CLEE

Ludlow ●

WYRE

① Wellington Hay
② Lythwood
③ Bentley Hay
④ Shirlett
⑤ Morfe
⑥ Hawkhurst
⑦ Bushmoor

miles   10

km   15

park. In 1400–1 there were 245 horses including 151 mares at the Clun stud. They ate large amounts of hay and oats, and 'at the time of leaping the mares' the stallions were fed a pea bread. These were cosseted animals, kept warm in the winter with blankets in candle-lit stables and treated with sulphur, fur, pig fat, olive oil, and honey when they had mange.

Only the aristocracy kept and hunted deer. Domesday Book records how

A STAG HUNT
Hunting and parks remained indicators of gentry status long after the end of the Middle Ages. The aspiration of Francis Jenkes, an Eaton under Heywood farmer, to that rank is suggested by his choice of this wall painting to decorate one of the main rooms in his new house of c. 1600, New Hall.

DOVECOT AT ASTON MUNSLOW
In the garden of the White House stands a ruinous stone dovecot, probably medieval. This 1947 view clearly shows the nest holes, of which there were c. 500, each with an alighting ledge. Eggs and squabs (young pigeons) were collected from a potence, a ladder which revolved around a fixed central post.

whenever King Edward the Confessor (1042-66) stayed at Marsley, a royal hunting lodge near Habberley, the sheriff of Shropshire had to find 36 men, presumably beaters, for eight days. During William the Conqueror's reign (1066-87) vast tracts of countryside were designated as royal 'forest', areas where forest law as well as common law had to be obeyed. Forest law was devoted to one end: the protection of deer and their habitat – wood, scrub, and grazing land. Many traditional aspects of land use were thereby prohibited and penalties for those caught breaking forest law, for instance by cutting down trees, were severe, the poacher facing blinding or hanging. The area under forest law was gradually extended, and in the late 12th century a third of England was deemed forest. Much of south and east Shropshire was forest, and the inclusion of Much Wenlock and Bridgnorth in Shirlett forest shows how 'forest' was a legal concept, and that while forests did include large tracts of wood and waste they also encompassed settlements and their fields. Forest law was so restrictive and unpopular that from the late 12th century areas began to pay to be released from it or 'disafforested'. In 1301 Shropshire's forests were drastically reduced, and little more than the king's own woods remained as forest. Although some of these, like Shirlett, remained forests for another 300 years or more, forest law was never again the contentious issue that it had previously been.

A few of the king's favourites bought areas of forest from him to hold as private forests, usually called 'chases', as in Cannock Chase in Staffordshire. Usually, however, a lord who wished to hunt deer did so by creating a park, enclosing woodland and pasture with a high 'pale' or fence. Until about 1270 the king kept a tight rein on park numbers, but thereafter large numbers of new parks were created. Most were of 50-100 acres, like Acton Burnell park, enlarged from 40 a. to 80 a. in 1280, and Yockleton, said in 1300 to comprise 70 a. A park might also contain the lord's best timber trees and his most valuable stock, all watched over by a resident parker. Nevertheless pales and parkers were ineffective against determined rustlers, and when Myddle park was broken into about 1314 not only deer but also 24 mares, 16 colts, and 80 oxen were stolen.

Other delicacies besides deer were raised mainly or exclusively by lords. Rabbits, introduced into England in the 12th century, were kept in special enclosures called warrens and remained costly and prized throughout the Middle Ages. Lords also bred hares, partridges, and pheasants. Pigeons, too, were bred for their meat, and from the 13th century dovecots or pigeon houses were a usual feature of manorial farms. At Kinnerley in the 1330s the pigeons were fed on oats in the winter; 232 were produced in 1336-7, 146 of which were sold. The dovecot at Blakemere was larger, and in 1410 supplied 1,222 pigeons to Lady Talbot's household. From the 13th century most manors also had one or more fishponds containing bream, perch, pike, roach, and tench, and – from the 14th or 15th century – carp. Fish breeding was well developed, and stock was moved long distances, packed in wet grass in canvas-lined barrels. In 1275, for instance, 100 live female bream were taken the 30 miles from Ellesmere to the king's fishponds at Church Stretton. The most commonly available fish were eels, taken in vast quantities in traps from the county's rivers, and herrings, caught in the Irish sea and available (salted) from fishmongers in Shrewsbury such as Nicholas of Grimsby. Unlike pond fish, eels and herrings could be afforded by all but the poorest peasants.

Chickens were widely kept for their eggs, and peasants gave large numbers of eggs and chickens to their lords in return for access to woods. Around 1300 the villagers of Clive were paying 300 hens each Christmas to the lord of Wem, and the villagers of Upton Magna and Haughton 33 hens and 170 eggs to their lord. Millers sometimes kept poultry on a commercial basis, and about 1280 the Ruyton miller kept cocks, hens, capons, geese, ganders, chickens, and ducks.

Good Times and Bad

The Normans came to a prosperous country with a growing population. Between 1066 and the early 14th century the growth continued, from perhaps two million to five or six million – a massive threefold increase in just over 250 years.

More food was required, and more land than ever before (and for long after) was under the plough by the early 1300s. The fields around existing settlements expanded outwards as land was cleared and brought into arable cultivation, the process being reflected in field names like 'stockings' (land covered with tree stumps), 'ridding' (land rid of trees), and 'brand' or 'burnt lands'. New settlements grew up in areas of cleared woodland and on heaths, often with the encouragement of the lord of the manor who would increase his rent income thereby. Sometimes settlers were attracted by a lord's offer of low rents while the land was brought into cultivation, or of 'free' tenure, as at Oaks – a telling place name – near Pontesbury, in the 12th century and at Berrington, Longnor, Smethcott and Woolstaston in the 13th. Freeholders enjoyed certain tenurial advantages over villeins, notably that they were not required to do labour services for the lord of the manor, and their land was, in effect, their own, to dispose of as they wished. Between the 13th and 14th centuries single freehold farms multiplied wherever there was ample land to be taken up, and many of Shropshire's farms called 'Woodhouse' originated at that time. Frequently such isolated farm buildings were contained within a broad shallow moat and a stout fence or thorn hedge, intended to deter rustlers and grain thieves.

The ever-increasing need for more arable land caused a steady reduction in the amount of common woods, heaths, and moors and greater pressure on those that remained. Disputes over common rights increased, and commons that were shared, or 'intercommoned', by several communities began to be partitioned between them. In 1190, for instance, Shrewsbury abbey and Wenlock priory divided woods on the Wrekin which their tenants had previously intercommoned. Woodland boundaries often took the form of linear clearings, called 'trenches'; Trench Way, today a busy road in north Telford, originated as just such a boundary in the 13th century.

On the whole the 250 years following the Norman Conquest were good ones for lords. Demand for food and other commodities was growing, prices rising, and cheap labour abounded. Thus in the 13th century many lords ran their estates directly using managers such as reeves and bailiffs, rather than taking the safer, but less profitable, option of leasing them out. High rents could be got, however, for such land as the lord did not wish to farm himself, and much land which had formerly been unprofitable 'waste' began to be rented and dragged into production by those unable to find better land. For most peasants, however, subsistence was all that could be hoped for, and genuine hardship, even starvation, was never far away. The average peasant family needed about 10 a. to subsist, and in the 13th century probably between a third and a half of the county's peasants had holdings of that size or less. At Prees in 1298 over half of the 85 holdings were of 5 a. or less, and another dozen were of 5 a. to 10 a. Only about 20 families had 10 a. or more and, of those, few had over 20 a. For families without sufficient land to grow food, money had to be got to purchase it, whether by farm work or such occupations as peat cutting, charcoal burning, or pottery making.

In the early 14th century there were signs of change. A continued demand for land meant that high rents could be obtained, and landlords began to prefer the security and ease of a rental income. As the century wore on, punctuated by a sequence of natural catastrophes, that trend became more marked, and by about 1425 the great estates had little land in hand apart from studs.

The first catastrophe was the 'agrarian crisis' of 1315-22, when farmers faced calamitous harvest failures and sheep and cattle plagues. Those with few or no reserves to draw on died or left their holdings to wander, probably fruitlessly, in search of a living elsewhere. At Adderley 20 of the manor's peasants left in 1316-17 'because of their poverty and the dearth of corn', and there were 34 vacant holdings by 1322. For many people things did not

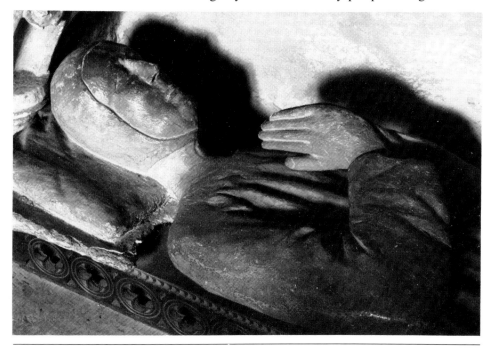

A MEDIEVAL FARMER?
In the chancel of Eaton under Heywood church, at the foot of Wenlock Edge, is this fine early 14th-century oak effigy of a layman. He was probably a tenant of the lord of the manor (the prior of Wenlock) or the lord's bailiff; the bailiff would have run the demesne farm and supervised the manorial tenants.

improve much in the 1320s or 1330s, and the crisis of 1315-22 seems to have fatally disrupted a system that previously had just managed to support what in reality was too high a population level. Excuses made to the Crown's tax assessors in 1341 show what a poor state agricultural communities were in, especially on the poorer lands in south and west Shropshire. At Cold Weston all but two of the tenants had left their holdings to avoid paying the tax, and in the previous year four successive parsons had resigned because it was such a poor living. A similar story was told at 20 other places: at Cardington, hit in 1340 by sheep disease and harvest failure, 20 tenants had left, while at Tugford it was said that poverty prevented the tenants from tilling their land (presumably because they could not afford new stock or seed corn) and six had become beggars.

The decisive blow to the old order came in 1348-9, when the Black Death swept the country, killing a third of the population in a little over a year. It reached Shropshire in the spring of 1349, its progress marked by notes of vacant lands and falling rent rolls in manorial records. The epidemic was at its worst during the summer and autumn: at Kinnerley 14 tenements, about a quarter of the total, lay unoccupied in September, while at Prees 22 new tenants took up empty holdings at the manorial court held in October rather than the usual one or two. At Wrockwardine the manor's rent roll fell from £20 to £2 'because the tenants are dead'. Plague broke out again in 1361-2 and 1369, and in fact the population of England remained at the level to which it had been cut in 1349 until the early 16th century. The decades after the Black Death saw drastic changes in the countryside. On manors, like Wrockwardine, with good soil new tenants could easily be found to take over dead mens' lands, but elsewhere land lay vacant in spite of being offered at a lower rate. Lords began to put unwanted arable land down to grass and to increase their herds and flocks, and for some that proved a profitable change.

In the 15th century gentry families and wealthy townsmen began to be attracted by the profits that could be made from farming and to take leases, and by the 16th century such men were among the county's leading farmers. Cases are also known of prominent villagers, or groups of them, taking leases. Alberbury priory's grange, or farm, at Pecknall was leased to four peasants in 1373, and the demesne arable at Ruyton-XI-Towns in 1409 to a group of tenants headed by the vicar. Usually those leases were for money although in the 14th and 15th centuries some included a profit-sharing element, the lord taking a quarter or a third of the harvested produce.

Pastoral farming offered the greatest profit, and lords often kept grassland in hand long after they had let their arable. Even if a lord did not need the grazing or hay for his own stock it could be let as accommodation land or sold as a cash crop to others. Efforts were being made to improve grassland at this time, with better drainage and the clearance of thorns and brambles. Such an investment was only worthwhile when a man held his land separately as a fenced or hedged close, rather than as a share of common meadow or pasture. Increasingly men began to inclose their grassland, although that often led to disputes when others claimed that the inclosure damaged their common rights. Usually, however, once grassland was inclosed it stayed inclosed.

Inclosures also began to be made in the open fields, and lords, lessees, and peasants all began to build up blocks of strips through purchases and exchanges. Open fields disappeared first around small hamlets where the strips were shared between just a few farmers, as at Allfield, in Condover, where Thomas Botte was buying up other men's strips and making inclosures in 1430, and at Great Bretchell, in Cardeston, where land held by eight tenants in 1379 was leased as pasture to a single tenant in the 15th century. As such men began to plant hedges and dig ditches around their lands the modern farming landscape began to evolve.

New types of tenure began to replace the outmoded 'customary' tenure by which men had held their land partly in return for working on the lord's land. In the 14th century peasants began to hold their land for a set term recorded in a lease or a copy of the agreement recorded on the manor's court roll (hence a 'copyhold' holding). Many of the old dues, such as the payment of a hen to the lord for the privilege of access to the manor's woodland, died out. The ones that lords managed to keep going longest – sometimes into the 16th century and beyond – were the more valuable ones, such as pannage, that is payment for any pigs put into the manor's woods, and heriot, where the lord took the best chattel (usually a beast) from the goods of a dead tenant.

1540-1750

The two centuries after the dissolution of the monasteries were important ones in the development of agriculture. The county's farmers began to specialize in producing those commodities best suited to their farms, one of the most notable developments being the growth of dairy farming in north Shropshire. More land was added to farms as thousands of acres of waste and common were brought into regular cultivation, and in many areas inclosure led to the disappearance of open fields and the emergence of the landscape of today. The average village farmer became more prosperous, with improved diet and housing. Nevertheless, although they were centuries of expansion and progress, crises did occur. Crop failure remained a threat for farmers and harvest failures were particularly severe in the 1590s and 1620s. Nor was the period free of animal disease, and cattle plague in the 1740s hit Shropshire's livestock trade badly.

Landlords and estates

If the Middle Ages ended at any particular event it was with the Reformation of the English church, which began in the 1530s and 1540s with Henry VIII's dissolution of monasteries, hospitals, collegiate churches, and chantries. For centuries those foundations had controlled or influenced many aspects of rural life through their role as landowners. At the Dissolution, however, that land, along with the monasteries themselves, was seized by the Crown. By and large the Crown did not retain the land for long, but sold it, either directly or via speculators, to new owners.

A considerable number of the new owners came from the gentry class, substantial and respected local families, already emerging as the most important rural landowning class with the break-up of many of the great countrywide aristocratic estates. Families such as the Actons of Aldenham, the Charltons of Apley Castle, and the Corbetts of Longnor improved their estates by acquiring properties which adjoined existing ones. Others, such as wealthy merchants and townsmen, effectively bought into the gentry class by purchasing rural estates. They included Thomas Ireland, a Shrewsbury mercer who bought Albrighton; Thomas Lawley, a Wenlock wool merchant who bought the priory there; and Roger Smyth, a Bridgnorth burgess who

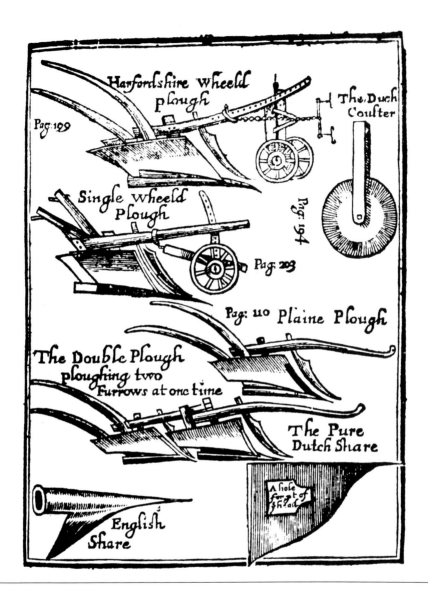

Labels within illustration: Harfordshire wheeld plough; Pag: 199; The Dutch Coulter; Single wheeld Plough; Pag: 194; Pag: 203; Pag: 110 Plaine Plough; The Double Plough ploughing two Furrows at one time; The Pure Dutch Share; English Share; A sole forgd of sheat

AN EARLY FARMING TREATISE

A steady trickle of printed farming manuals began to appear in England from the early 16th century, addressed principally to the gentleman farmer. Some were polemical works, designed to promote a new idea, technique, or tool. Others, however, such as Walter Blith's The Improver Improved *(1653) from which the above illustration is taken, were more in the nature of handbooks to current practice.*

bought much former church property around Bridgnorth. Lawyers too had the money to invest in landed estates, that conferred a standing in society that their profession did not. By 1620 about fifty families were added to the substantial gentry of Shropshire. Not all continued to prosper and some, like the Haywards, had later to sell up. Gradually, however, a new order and hierarchy was established at the apex of rural society, an order that was to survive, despite the rise and fall of individual families, until the end of the Victorian age.

Increasingly landowners sought to raise their income from tenanted lands. Income from copyholds, the most common form of tenure, was often fixed and relatively poor, and many lords attempted to convert such tenures to leaseholds or at least to 'copyholds at will', whereby rents and other dues could be periodically raised rather than being permanently fixed. New land, such as that taken from former commons, was usually leased from the outset. From the mid 16th century, in a further move to keep up their incomes, lords began to give shorter leases, often of 21 years, rather than the 50 which had been common earlier in the century. For tenants a more secure prospect was a lease for three lives or 99 years. Unlike those in the midlands and eastern England, where economic annual rents ('rack rents') were introduced at an early date, tenants in Shropshire usually owed only a small sum ('reserved rent') to their landlord each year, having paid a substantial 'entry fine' when they took their property. Although in the late 17th and early 18th century some estates did begin to introduce 'rack rents', so called because they could be racked or raised each year, in 1750 they remained a far less common form of farm tenure than life leaseholds.

A changing countryside

As has been seen, in some places the open fields began to shrink in the 14th and 15th centuries as farmers began to inclose blocks of strips. In the early 1600s the pace of inclosure picked up. Sometimes lords were the promoters, inclosing their lands and encouraging others to do likewise. At Corfton William Baldwyn initiated exchanges with Charles Foxe, the manor's other major landowner, and by the mid 17th century the township was almost entirely inclosed, and the Baldwyns adopted a similar policy at Diddlebury and Siefton in the 1630s. Elsewhere villagers took the lead, as at Lilleshall in

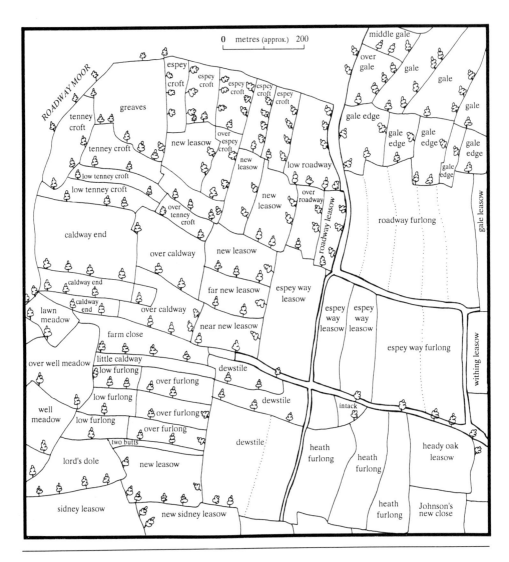

INCLOSURES AT KYNNERSLEY ABOUT 1780

Piecemeal inclosure of Kynnersley's open fields had been going on since at least the 1580s. Shown here is the area north-west of the village; the oldest inclosures lie furthest from the village and have trees growing in their hedgerows. Nearer the village inclosures are more recent: hedgerows are treeless, and some open field strips survive. Repeated field names show where larger units, such as furlongs, have been subdivided.

the late 17th century where William Leveson-Gower's tenants petitioned him that their strips lay inconveniently dispersed and would benefit from inclosure. First, however, exchanges would be required in order to 'lay their ground together and to make each others' farms convenient to them'.

Although generally beneficial the inclosure of open fields was not entirely so, for as the strips disappeared so did common grazing on the fallow land; that change was particularly damaging to the smallholders and cottagers without closes to keep their animals in. With increasing pressure on the remaining common, grazing 'stints' began to be introduced, as early as the 1550s around the Weald Moors and more widely in the 17th century. A 'stint' was a maximum number of animals that a man might put onto the commons, determined by the size of his property. At Lilleshall in 1617 the stint was established as eight 'beasts' – horses or cattle – and 60 sheep for every holding of 50 acres or so, and proportionately fewer for smaller holdings. At the same time that the open fields were being inclosed so too were thousands of acres of waste and common land, especially from the mid 16th century as the population began to increase once more and landowners began to improve their estates. Woods were cleared and replaced by fields, and at Clun in 1575-6 an octogenarian recalled how that had happened to over 600 a. of Clun forest in his lifetime. At Myddle, once 'beautified with many famous woods', fellings were organized by successive lords of the manor. Divlin wood went in the late 15th century, Brandwood and Holloway Hills wood a generation later, and Myddlewood from the mid 16th century. In clearing woodland the landowner not only gained farmland, he also realized a substantial capital gain from sale of the timber.

In a few instances the same motives led to the splitting up of medieval parks. There again woods might be cleared and the previously open parkland landscape divided into fields. That process is vividly caught on a map of Tilstock, where two tenants are shown felling trees in the former deer park *c.* 1600.

For the most part, however, existing parks were used more intensively, and many entirely new ones were created. In a number of cases lords imparked lands allotted to them when common woods or wastes were inclosed. Thus when, in 1625, Shirlett forest, south of Barrow, was divided between those with rights in it, John Weld of Willey immediately imparked his 410-a. share, although he already had a park in Willey barely a kilometre away. The new park's management went hand in hand with the old one's, and Weld's investments in them demonstrate the economic role of parks at

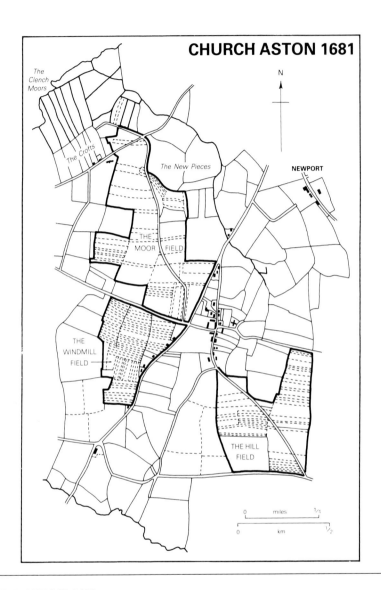

CHURCH ASTON 1681

The Clench Moors

The Crofts

The New Pieces

NEWPORT

THE MOOR FIELD

THE WINDMILL FIELD

THE HILL FIELD

N

| 0 | miles | 1/4 |
| 0 | km | 1/2 |

CHURCH ASTON 1681
The manor's three fields remained open until inclosed in the early 18th century. They show a feature seen elsewhere in the county — long strips running from furlong to furlong. In the northern part of the manor much of the moorland had already been inclosed in 1681. No woodland survived, and the only trees would have been in hedgerows.

30

that time. They were stocked with cattle, deer, and horses, fishponds were made, and swans and bees introduced. At the same time traditional woodland management continued, with coppice wood and timber being grown in woods that fattened pigs in the autumn. In many parks much greater emphasis was placed on stock rearing or dairy farming, and in Shropshire, as elsewhere, lords were 'making their deer leap over the pale to give bullocks place'. That was so at Cardeston in the mid 16th century and at

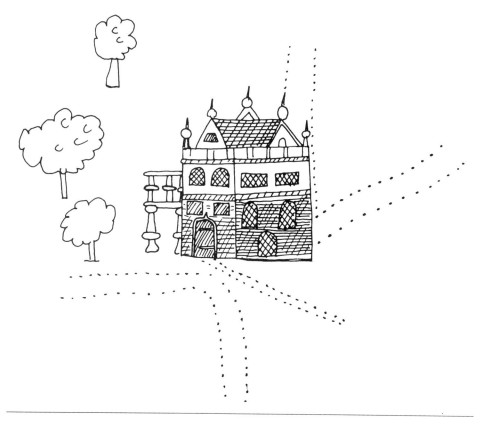

LILLESHALL PARK LODGE 1679
Lilleshall park, created in the Middle Ages, still contained deer in the early 18th century. The lodge, shown on a map of 1679, had a balcony (on left) from which the hunt, or simply the parkland view, could be appreciated.

Minsterley a century later, while in 1617 the Council in the Marches of Wales recorded that Sir Charles Foxe refused to show 'by what title he doth hold Oakly Park and keepeth more sheep and cattle than deer'.

Parks of the 16th and 17th century, however, were not purely functional

THE DUKE'S DRIVE, KYNNERSLEY
The early 17th century saw major attempts to drain and improve the fen-like Weald Moors, between Wellington and Newport. Much remained undone, however, and a second major campaign to bring the land into profitable cultivation was needed in the early 19th century. It was then that the Duke's Drive was laid out, running west from Kynnersley and dividing Wrockwardine Moor (on left) from Sidney Moor.

and, as before and later, a park conferred prestige and drew attention to the owner's social rank. In a number of instances parks were made or enlarged to embellish new or remodelled houses, as at Plaish, Moreton Corbet, and Upton Cressett. The work might involve the removal of tenants' houses or the diversion of roads, and in such cases the park was designed to be more than protection for the lord's beasts and woods. It was also conceived as a wide surrounding paradise, almost invariably still furnished with deer, the intended sport of the owner and his most favoured guests.

Landowners were also draining land, especially in north Shropshire, and one of the biggest transformations was the reclamation by 1650 of perhaps 2,500 a. of the fen-like Weald Moors. The motive, of course, was profit, although heavy investment might be required. In 1539 Sir Richard Brereton bought a 200-a. marsh in Prees called Dogmoor, so 'miry and deep of water that no cattle could feed or pasture thereon'. It was virtually worthless, but after Brereton had spent between £490 and £666 draining it and laying it to fields Dogmoor was said to be worth £26 13s. 4d. a year. Inclosure of heathlands was cheaper, although they tended to have sandier, lighter, and less fertile soils than former wood or marsh lands. Heathland inclosure became more common from the mid 17th century, with much of the ground being put down to rye, barley, and later wheat.

Occasionally lords rode rough-shod over commoners and ignored their rights when inclosing land, but by and large tenants seem to have been treated fairly. Often they received some newly inclosed land in lieu of common rights, or else alternative common grazing was provided. Inevitably, as the population rose and the surviving commons shrank, stints were introduced, as in the open fields, to prevent over-grazing.

Commons were also shrinking at that time as the poor built cottages on them, and although each cottager might inclose only an acre or two of common the cumulative total could be considerable. In Stanton Lacy the commons were gradually reduced in the 17th and 18th centuries in that way: in 1732 there were 34 squatters, in 1747 there were 40. Squatting on the commons was a particular feature of industrial areas such as the east Shropshire coalfield and the Clee Hills, to which workers migrated to find employment in the quarries, mines, and ironworks. About 1600 much of Broseley's commons disappeared as immigrant miners, considered by the dispossessed locals as 'lewd persons, the scums and dregs of many counties', moved in and built cottages in what became known as Broseley Wood. These cottages were small and primitive, at best two-up and two-down, and were probably similar to farm labourers' cottages throughout the county. They stood in contrast to the houses of successful yeomen farmers, which in the 16th and 17th centuries became larger and better appointed. Many farmhouses gained more rooms by having bigger ground plans, by the insertion of floors across medieval open halls, and by the making of garretts

CATHERTON COMMON
Looking west across Catherton Common, a landscape of irregular squatters' enclosures and the pock-marks of 'bell-pits', infilled mine shafts. The squatter settlement was known as Lubberlands, after a mythical land of plenty without labour. This, essentially a landscape of the 17th and 18th centuries, contrasts vividly with that of the Farlow Enclosure beyond. That, with its grid-like fields, was created about 1815 by the earl of Craven's inclosure of common land.

or 'cock lofts' in the roofspace. Those extra rooms allowed the farmer and his family greater privacy, servants and labourers to be accommodated, and produce to be stored and processed. In the farmyard, however, little had changed since the Middle Ages, although dairies may have become more common, especially in north Shropshire.

Arable farming

In the 16th and 17th centuries Shropshire's agriculture remained predominantly pastoral, although arable production did increase with the inclosure of commons, wastes, and open fields, and following the adoption of more flexible systems of husbandry. In the mid 16th century a rough balance existed between winter corn (wheat and rye) and spring corn (barley and oats). Where open fields survived, organization of the arable land could be simple: at Cleobury North in 1600 winter corn grew in Oakwood field, oats in Stable field, and Haymers field lay fallow. After 1600 an increasing proportion of barley was grown, especially in central, northern, and eastern Shropshire. Much was malted for brewing, especially around the larger towns, although after bad harvests brewers were sometimes forced to release barley onto the market for use as bread corn. Barley was also increasingly used in the 17th century as animal feed. Of the two winter corns rye seems to have been more widely grown in the earlier 17th century although towards 1700 the position reversed as wheat was sown on the 'strong' heavy land recently inclosed from marsh and woodland. Pulses, especially peas, were increasingly sown in the 17th century usually at the expense of oats. As in the Middle Ages they were cropped when dry, mainly for use as a fodder crop, although the poor did sometimes make a kind of bread from them.

A feature of the period was the increase in ley farming, a form of convertible or 'up-and-down' husbandry whereby the fertility of arable land was maintained or improved by putting it down to grass for a few years and grazing it. In their newly inclosed fields farmers rotated their animals and crops and a genuine form of mixed farming began to develop in areas best suited to it. Farmers on the sandy soils of east Shropshire, then the county's leading cereal producing region, led the way to mixed farming with the development by 1650 of a regime centred on the production of sheep and corn. Elsewhere in the county – as along the Severn and Tern, and in Corve

Dale for example — similar practices grew up, albeit with local variations such as the raising of cattle rather than sheep. A class of prosperous yeomen emerged in south Shropshire in the mid 17th century, who had large acreages under crops, ran substantial herds of cattle, and in many cases kept sizeable flocks of sheep too. Thomas Stedman of Stanton Lacy, for instance, had 26 a. of winter corn and 75 a. of spring corn ripening in July 1725, in ground kept in good heart by the application of dung, marl, and lime, and ploughed by his 16 oxen. He had a herd of 50 cattle providing both dairy produce and store cattle for the beef market, and he also reared and fattened pigs and sheep and bred horses.

A LATE 18TH-CENTURY FARMYARD SCENE AT TWYFORD
A remarkably detailed late 18th-century farmyard scene, from a map of Twyford, near West Felton, south-west of Oswestry. The harvest is being gathered, the cart-horses watered, pigs fed, and (apparently) the cow milked. Various kinds of poultry peck around, while the farmer's dog sits outside his kennel, to the left of the house. Perhaps it is the farmer himself who stands, besmocked and whip in hand, in the centre of the picture.

A second important innovation, very much linked to the appearance of ley farming, was the growing of fodder crops such as clover and sainfoin. They were nitrogen fixers, adding to soil fertility and yielding heavy crops of hay and good grazing on the 'aftermath', the growth left after the hay had been cut. Clover was included in rotations in the east and in the Teme valley by 1700, in the east Shropshire coalfield by 1720, and in the heathlands by 1740. Soon after, and firstly on the farms of gentlemen enthusiasts, turnips began to be cultivated as a fodder crop rather than as a garden vegetable. They could be grown on light soils, previously of limited potential; the sheep that fed off them during the winter in the fields where they grew dunged the ground at the same time and thus prepared it for next year's barley crop. Potatoes, a field crop in parts of England by 1650, also first appeared in Shropshire in the mid 18th century through the instigation of the gentry.

Of the industrial crops, flax and hemp were widely grown in small plots attached to houses. For the poor the processing of the crops – the respective raw materials for linen and for rope and coarse cloth – was an important cottage industry. In Cardington, for instance, 17 people were presented in 1610 for steeping hemp and flax in a brook and thereby polluting it. By contrast dye crops like saffron, woad, and madder, which were much promoted in the later 16th century by agricultural writers, were apparently little cultivated in Shropshire. Hop cultivation expanded rapidly after 1650, especially in south Shropshire: Walter Pooler of Neen Sollars had 12,000 hop poles in 1746, and John Smith of Boraston 20,000 in 1750. Fruit growing continued to be widespread, and leaseholders were sometimes required to plant fruit trees in hedgerows. Much of the fruit was eaten, although in south Shropshire it was cider apples that were grown, and there, as in Herefordshire, a substantial brewing industry developed in the later 17th century.

In 16th-century Shropshire oxen continued to be used for ploughing. There was no distinct county breed, but the Shropshire ox was noted for its large dewlap, the loose fold of skin hanging from the beast's throat. On heavy soils teams could be large: in 1550 John Perton of Ledwyche had one comprising eight oxen and two steers. Teams of that size were beyond the means of smaller farmers who therefore hired animals. Thus in 1550 John Reynolds of Down (in Lydbury North) owed money to two men for the hire of two yokes of bullocks. Horses were beginning to be used to plough by the 1660s, and in the light-soiled parishes of east Shropshire the horse had supplanted the ox by 1700. Elsewhere the change occurred more slowly and in areas like Clun, with difficult soils, the ox remained the main draught animal in the mid 18th century. One encouragement to the use of horses for ploughing was the appearance from the mid 17th century of larger and stronger breeds such as the Old English Black as powerful draught horses were imported from the Low Countries and crossed with local stock.

The main farm vehicle in the 1550s was the two-wheeled wain, drawn by oxen and used for such tasks as corn and muck carrying. Gradually thereafter horse-drawn carts gained popularity, and by the later 17th century they had supplanted wains for all farm work. In the early 18th century the more prosperous farmers began to use heavy four-wheeled wagons. Although cumbersome in the field they enabled farmers to move their produce efficiently in bulk to market.

Pastoral farming

By 1540 cattle had perhaps replaced sheep as the commonest animals on the county's farms; certainly that was so in north Shropshire. Both dairy and beef farming had become more profitable as the standard of living rose and with it the demand for milk, butter, cheese, and meat. Already differing regional emphases in cattle farming could be seen. Dairy farming was most pronounced in the north, especially in the parishes bordering Cheshire, and it was also a feature of the coalfield area where the growing industrial population produced a steady demand for dairy produce. By contrast, in the Clun area the raising of 'stores', bullocks later sold on to be fattened, predominated.

In the following century north Shropshire's dairy industry grew alongside Cheshire's to national prominence, and by the 1720s 'great quantities' of Cheshire cheese were made not only in Cheshire but in the adjoining parts of Shropshire, Staffordshire and Lancashire too. Richard Furber of Shavington may be instanced as an example of the wealthy dairy farmer. In 1660 he had a herd of 62 cows, a bull, 3 bull calves, 30 sucking calves, 25 yearlings, 15 two-year-olds and two oxen. In store he had several tons of cheese worth £168, a large sum at a time when a cow cost about £2 7s. His cattle were probably of the black Longhorned variety common to Cheshire and other northern counties and yielding excellent milk for cheese making.

Between 1550 and 1650 there was also an increase in beef fattening on river meadows and in fenny areas like the Weald Moors. By the end of the 17th century grassland in Shropshire was being 'floated' — water from an adjoining watercourse being run over it during the winter via a system of ditches and sluices. The water deposited silt rich in nutrients and protected the pasture from frosts, and thus encouraged an early and strong growth of grass. Not surprisingly, given the capital outlay involved, it was the gentry who first promoted commercial fatstock production and the improvement of pastures.

Shropshire's sheep maintained their medieval reputation for fine wool, especially those from around Shrewsbury and Bridgnorth. In the 17th century demand for this began to fall as textile producers demanded coarser and longer wool, but an emerging market for mutton helped to maintain the numbers kept. Among the chief types were the old Shropshire, horned and with a black or mottled face and legs, and the Longmyndian, nimble, hardy and also black faced. The largest flocks were on the extensive upland commons of south and north-west Shropshire, and the Stiperstones, the Long Mynd, the Long forest, Clun forest, and the Clee Hills were all established sheep walks. Large flocks were also found on the heathlands of the north-east, on the Weald Moors, and on farms in eastern Shropshire that adopted a mixed sheep-corn regime. No longer were there great capitalist wool producers, such as the earl of Arundel in the Middle Ages; instead there were large numbers of farmers with flocks of 75 or 100 head. After 1550 sheep were probably rarely milked, though poor people with just a few animals may have continued the practice.

Pig keeping in those parts of the county with extensive woods and commons continued to be important in the mid 16th century but thenceforward, as woods were felled and commons inclosed, opportunities declined. Instead pig production was undertaken commercially by large-scale farmers who kept pigs at least in part on by-products of their main farming enterprises, such as whey on dairy farms. Other pig foods included barley mash, malt, dried peas, and the dregs of ale barrels. Under such a regime, and perhaps with selective breeding, a pig more like the modern animal emerged. About 1750 Shropshire hogs were claimed as England's best, those of the north-east being characterized as 'large, broadset, and weighty'.

1750-1875

The later 18th century and the first three quarters of the 19th century form a period of relative prosperity in British agriculture. At first export bounties pushed up grain prices, while population growth and almost a quarter of a century of war (1793-1815) against France and her allies increased domestic demand and raised prices, rents, and land values to unprecedented levels. Inclosure of commons and the remaining open fields was stimulated, arable farming expanded, and new farming machines and animal breeds appeared – albeit later in Shropshire than in some other regions – in what amounted to an agricultural revolution. Farmers, whether freeholders or tenants, continued to prosper in the mid 19th century, especially from 'high farming' with its emphasis on the rearing and feeding of livestock as part of a mixed farming regime. Many farmhouses were built or altered to allow a more genteel lifestyle. Save in exceptional circumstances, however, the farm labourer did not share in the period's prosperity; wages were kept low, housing remained bad, and after 1834 the workhouse overshadowed the old age of all but the most fortunate or rigidly provident.

Landlords, farmers, and labourers

The increasing profit to be had from land meant that wherever possible families held on to their estates, and of the greater estates only the Craven and the Apley Park ones were sold off during this period. With the more modest gentry estates, of 6,000 acres or less, it was otherwise, and many changed hands as families were ruined by expensive living or died out. Nevertheless there was a good demand for those properties from the holders of commercial or industrial fortunes, such as ironmasters, bankers, businessmen, and slavers, who were keen for the entrée to county society provided by a landed estate.

If contemporary opinion may be trusted, the tenant farmers of the earlier 19th century were superior in intellect and education to many of their predecessors. That was at least partly due to self-improvement by reading and the attendance of lectures and meetings. In 1841 the Wenlock Agricultural Reading Society was formed; it had reading rooms and a library, in which priority was given to books on agriculture. Many of its members were local farmers, who paid an annual subscription of 6*s*. Ironically it was also at Much Wenlock in 1884 that the squire's wife, Lady Catherine Milnes Gaskell, cherished condescending notions of the ideal farming family. In a monthly magazine called *The Nineteenth Century* she depicted the tenants of 'a farm that pays' as simple people educated narrowly for the work they had to do, leading a life of incessant toil, domestic drudgery, and cheeseparing frugality. Without intellectual interests (beyond regular Bible reading) and strictly attentive to the habits of their forefathers, they disclaimed – in homely, unpolished speech – any political or other wider interests, content simply to affirm their reverence for the

TWIN WHITE OXEN
A pair of twin white oxen, owned by James Ackers, of Heath House, near Leintwardine, painted by the Ludlow artist William Gwynn in 1845. Although some working oxen were still to be seen in Shropshire in Queen Victoria's reign it seems more probable that Ackers, Tory M.P. for Ludlow 1841-7, kept the beasts for show.

queen. By then, however, such an outlook was more than half a century out of date and Lady Catherine's snobbery was effectively shown up in a reply to the magazine from Shropshire's leading farmer, John Bowen-Jones. He depicted 'a farm that pays' as one run by a modern tenant living 'a life of comfort and culture', who was at the same time 'a useful member of society'. The smock-coat farmer, Bowen-Jones concluded, was a figure of the past.

Tenant farmers' biggest outgoing was rent, believed in general to

JOHN COTES OF WOODCOTE
Cotes, a Whig, was M.P. for Shropshire from 1806 until his death in 1821. He was a founder member of the Shifnal Agricultural Society and an early member of the Board of Agriculture, to which he sent communications on potato cultivation. He is shown indicating a point of interest to the top-hatted man, presumably his steward: perhaps it is the tall leather collars, or housen, worn by the horses to protect their withers from driving rain.

represent a quarter of the farms' gross produce, although nearer to a third became increasingly usual. In the later 18th century, in an attempt to maintain income in an era of rising prices, almost all landlords were replacing leases with the annually reviewed, or 'racked', rents tried by some in an earlier period. In 1793 a commentator picked out the survival of leases on Lord Craven's south Shropshire estates as an oddity. The farmer's other outgoings included tithe payments to a rector or an impropriator and vicar, in theory ten per cent of gross produce but in practice often much less, and various taxes and local rates, especially poor rates. Those payments might account for a further tenth of farmers' residual income after the payment of rent.

Landlords were also introducing rack renting as a means of recouping investments in their tenants' farms, made in the expectation of increased long-term profit. Farms were enlarged and consolidated, provided with up-to-date farm buildings and houses, and were supplied with better roads and drainage. A spectacular example of how landlord expenditure might increase is provided by the Lilleshall estate, where between 1789 and 1804 it trebled. Rents on the estate rose alongside expenditure on improvements; they increased 50 per cent 1750-90, and by 1805 had doubled since 1750. In many cases, however, the improving landlord probably earned more in reputation than in cash profit, and many inventive and respected farming landlords – William Childe of Kinlet, William Wolryche Whitmore of Dudmaston, and the 2nd Lord Hill – left heavy mortgages to their successors. Hill, for instance, who died in 1875, was well known as an agriculturist and was a successful breeder on the scale that required commitment of capital, but his Hawkstone estate was run without financial control or discipline.

Despite the almost universal replacement of leasing by rack renting, on many large estates farms continued to be held by one family for generations. There was much mutual respect between landlord and tenant, and commentators noted the high state of cultivation on many tenanted farms. Moreover landowners and farmers were increasingly united by social forces. Sport was a powerful bond, field sports in particular providing those occasions of 'unceremonious intercourse' between gentry and farmers that engendered 'mutual admiration and respect'. Some local hunts were led by yeomen, and in 1843 the leading sports writer 'Nimrod' asserted that no other county in England showed more respect for the 'noble science' or had more sportsmen and well wishers among the 'higher orders' and the yeomen,

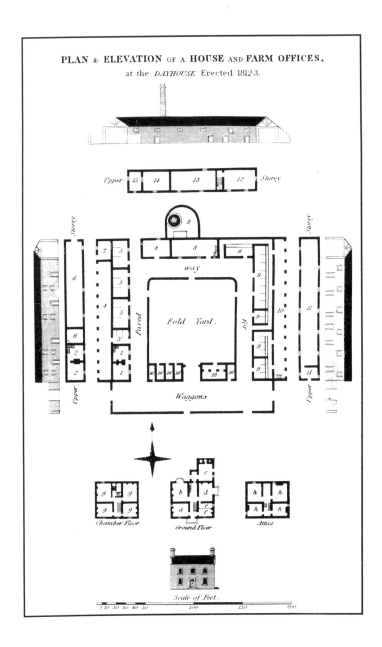

PLAN & ELEVATION OF A **HOUSE** AND **FARM OFFICES,**

at the *DAYHOUSE* Erected 1812-3.

Upper 15 14 13 12 *Storey*

Storey 7 5 8 8 9 *Storey*

6 way

4 5 9

Paved 5 *Fold Yard.* 9 10 11

6 9

2 1 9

2 1 16 16 16 16 16 9 11

Waggons

Upper *Upper*

9 9 | c | h h
b a | d e f | h h

Chamber Floor *Ground Floor* *Attics*

Scale of Feet.
5 10 20 30 40 50   100   150   200

44

the result being an 'excellent feeling' between tenant and landlord.

Politics, especially the protectionist cause as the free trade movement gathered strength in the 1840s, was a further bond between landlord and tenant. Protectionism gave an impetus to the formation of farmers' clubs. Two early ones (*c.* 1800) lay on the eastern, more agriculturally advanced, side of the county at Market Drayton and Shifnal, and by 1838 there was also a practical farmers' society at Ellesmere. Nevertheless it was the Wenlock Farmers' Club, founded in 1842, the year after the Wenlock Agricultural Reading Society, that was to provide the model for other clubs, such as those formed at Atcham (1843), Baschurch and Ruyton (by 1846), Ludlow (*c.* 1847), and Wellington (1843). Not all societies were a success, and in 1863, for example, farmers and gentlemen living around Bridgnorth wanted to join the Wenlock club when their own suspended operations.

Shropshire had no county agricultural society until 1810 when the Shropshire General Agricultural Society was formed. It organized – as did its successors – an annual stock show, but the events were restricted to subscribers and thus effectively closed to tenant farmers. That exclusiveness, and the inconvenience of a July show, led to the society's dissolution in 1823. A later society, the Shropshire Agricultural Association, was evidently in a similar condition by 1838 when Lord Darlington cancelled its annual dinner. The name of the Shropshire Practical Farmers' Association, which held its first show in 1840, indicates an intention to avoid harmful exclusiveness. By the 1850s, however, when it was known as the Shropshire Agricultural Society, it too was ailing. The Shropshire Chamber of Agriculture, formed in 1866, was destined to endure, and in 1874-5 was instrumental in setting up the Shropshire and West Midlands Agricultural Society, which held its first show at Shrewsbury in 1875.

DAYHOUSE FARM, CHERRINGTON, REBUILT 1812-13
One of many farms rebuilt on the Marquess of Stafford's estate in the early 19th century. The courtyard farm, with its central fold yard and steam powered machinery, then typified modern farm design. 1 Men servants' day rooms. 2 Men servants' sleeping rooms. 3 Hackney stable. 4 Implement shed. 5 Waggon horse stable. 6 Hay loft. 7 Tool house. 8 Barn and steam engine. 9 Feeding and cow tyings. 10 Turnip house. 11 Great granary and pay room, used for the annual agricultural dinner given by Lord Stafford. 12 Small granary. 13 Corn loft. 14 and 15 Straw lofts. 16 Pig styes, hen houses over. a Parlour. b Family room. c Brewhouse. d Kitchen. e Pantry. f Milk house. g Bedrooms. h Attics.

Dudleston Riots.

The following is a Copy of a Paragraph which appeared in the SALOPIAN JOURNAL, on WEDNESDAY the 8th of NOVEMBER; and as it seems calculated to open the Eyes of the poor deluded People at DUDLESTON HEATH, and to warn them of the imminent Danger of persisting in their late riotous and illegal Proceedings, it is hoped, that the advice it contains will not fail to produce the desired Effect :

" WE have been able to ascertain from undoubted authority, that our statement in last week's Paper, respecting the tumult at Dudleston-Heath was not quite correct, and we are happy to find that no life was lost on that occasion. The disturbance originated in an absurd notion, entertained by several people who have made encroachments and built cottages upon the Heath, that no one has any dominion there as Lord of the Manor (because ' it is' as they are pleased to term it ' a lawless place') and consequently, that the mere act of encroachment gives the occupant an immediate and absolute right to the soil. Under the influence of this sad delusion (in which, it is suspected, they have been secretly encouraged by evil and interested advisers, less ignorant than themselves) these poor people have attempted to resist the authority of an Act of Parliament, lately passed for the Inclosure of the Common Lands in Dudleston. We understand, that, soon after the passing of this Act, the Devisees of the late Earl of Powis, as Lords of the Manor, by their agent, humanely signified their intention of granting the Cottagers leases of their Cottages for a term of 21 years, or for two lives, at their own option, at very trifling annual rents. Of this the Cottagers were distinctly informed, and it is to be deeply regretted, that so benevolent an offer had not produced a very different effect upon their conduct. The Commissioner appointed to execute the powers of the Act has been menaced and obstructed in every stage of his duty, and, finding it utterly impossible to proceed in his operations of draining, he was ultimately compelled to solicit the aid of the civil Power. On Monday the 30th ult. six Magistrates and several Special Constables attended at Dudleston Heath. A large mob of women, and several men had previously assembled there. The women very soon evinced a determination to interrupt the progress of the workmen employed by the Commissioner in cutting the drains, and very assiduously replaced the sods as soon as they were dug out of the ground. The Magistrates endeavoured, by mild and temperate exhortations, to make these deluded people sensible of the illegality of their conduct, and of the dangerous consequences to which it would lead. They explained to them the terms of the Act of Parliament, and the kind intentions of the Lords of the Manor, but the admonitions of the Magistrates were wholly disregarded. The mob became more clamorous, and the women persisted in obstructing the Commissioner and his workmen. In this state of uproar the Proclamation

directed by the Riot Act was read. Nearly two hours elapsed; still the mob did not disperse, nor was there any considerable diminution of its numbers. The Magistrates then sent for a party of the Oswestry Rangers (Yeomanry Cavalry) under the command of Major Warrington, who being stationed within a few miles, promptly obeyed the call. On the arrival of the Cavalry another attempt was made by the Commissioner's workmen, supported by the Civil Power, to proceed with the Drain. This was vigorously resisted by the whole body of the mob, and in the course of the struggle many hard blows were struck by the constables, and returned by their opponents. A small portion of the Cavalry (dismounted) was then ordered to the assistance of the Constables, and by their joint exertions, three of the ring-leaders were secured. The rest of the men ran off. Two women were afterwards taken into custody, for persisting in their interruptions to the workmen; and all the prisoners were afterwards committed to the County Gaol, to take their Trials at the next Assizes for this serious offence, which by the Statute of the 1st GEORGE I. chap. 5, subjects the offenders to the penalty of DEATH. But whatever may be the fate of the unhappy prisoners, it is to be hoped, that their example will operate as a salutary caution to their misguided companions, who, (altho' they have eluded Justice for the present) will find in the end, that the laws are not to be trampled upon with impunity. It is also to be hoped, that as they have now had sufficient leisure to reflect upon the dangers they have escaped, they will endeavour to atone for their past misconduct, by their future peaceable demeanor, and that they will give the Magistrates such information as may lead to the discovery and conviction of their criminal abettors. But if, contrary to our sanguine hopes, the Cottagers should still be mad enough to persevere in their fruitless and unjustifiable opposition to the authority of a positive Act of Parliament, let them beware of the consequences of their temerity; and let them remember too, that the continuance of such unlawful means of violence will only serve to involve themselves in the same inevitable destruction, which it cannot fail to draw upon the heads of their wretched brethren now in custody. Much praise is due to the Magistrates for the exemplary firmness, patience, and forbearance, with which they appear to have acted, under very trying provocations, as well as to Major Warrington and the Detachment under his command, for their equally temperate and spirited conduct upon the occasion."

November 24th, 1809.

** It may also be proper to admonish the Cottagers, that, if they should again attempt to obstruct the Commissioner and his Workmen in the execution of their duty, they will not only subject themselves to the severest penalties of the law, but will also forfeit all claims to the indulgence of the Lords of the Manor.—If, therefore, they have any regard for their own interests, it behoves them seriously to consider this matter before it is too late.

SALTER, OSWESTRY, PRINTER

46

If landlords and tenants had much in common there were areas where their opinions diverged, especially over the letting of labourers' cottages and game preservation. Labourers' cottages were something which farmers wished to have included in their farm tenancies, to give them full control of their workforce. Landlords, however, at least from *c.* 1800, were well aware that this was not in the labourer's best interests and most seem to have resisted the farmers' demands. Game was increasingly well preserved from the mid 18th century, and rabbits became a particular irritant to farmers on many estates. The keenest game preserver of all was probably the 2nd Lord Forester. In 1870 Sir Baldwin Leighton noted in his diary: 'Last year 9,515 head of game were killed at Willey including only 800 rabbits. Lord F. who is now nearly 70 goes out shooting 2 or 3 times a week; he . . . is content with killing a moderate quantity on a fresh beat every day. Being very infirm from gout he is unable & goes about in a little carriage with a lot of attendants to get him over difficult places.'

The farm labourer's life was unenviable. Wages varied from place to place but were never much, in 1775 about 1*s.* a day with beer. Those on large farms often did best, receiving firewood and milk in addition to their wages, and perhaps a rent-free plot to grow potatoes in. It greatly improved a family's diet if a pig was kept, and some landowners and parsons sold piglets cheaply to the poor. If no pig was kept, meat was probably never seen in the labourer's house, and the diet would mainly comprise bread, potatoes, and a little cheese. French beans and potatoes were the commonest vegetables grown by labourers with gardens; carrots and onions were also quite widely cultivated. Cottage brewing was almost unknown by 1793.

The position of labourers worsened in the years after 1790 as wages failed to keep pace with the rapidly rising price of basic foodstuffs. When peace came in 1815 wages fell as farmers cut their costs. If Church Stretton parish was typical *c.* 1833, then daily rates had remained unchanged since 1822: 9*s.* a week in summer (with keep at harvest time) and winter. The labourer's wife, when employed, might earn 4*s.* a week at weeding or stone picking, and children under 16 might earn 2*s.* or 3*s.* Such additions, however, could

---

Opposition to inclosure from dispossessed cottagers, such as that described above which arose when the 228-a. heath at Dudleston, near Ellesmere, was inclosed, was rare in Shropshire. Despite the prominence given in the broadsheet to the possibility of the rioters receiving capital punishment, the three labourers and two labourers' wives arrested were in fact sentenced to a week in gaol.

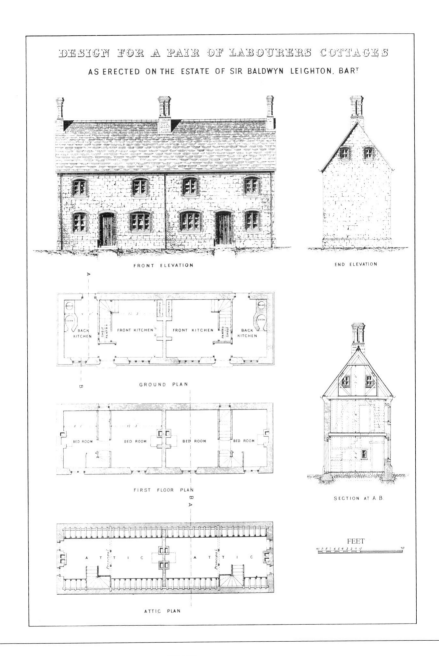

DESIGN FOR A PAIR OF LABOURERS COTTAGES

AS ERECTED ON THE ESTATE OF SIR BALDWYN LEIGHTON, BAR^T

FRONT ELEVATION

END ELEVATION

GROUND PLAN

FIRST FLOOR PLAN

SECTION AT A B

ATTIC PLAN

FEET

TALL COTTAGES, ALBERBURY

not be relied on: women were rarely employed in summer, and labourers' daughters were put into service and their sons informally apprenticed as soon as they could work, though wages were not usually paid before the last years of apprenticeship.

The houses of the rural poor were rarely better than hovels, whether they were squatters' dwellings on the edge of commons or rented village cottages. Squatters paid only a token 6*d*. or 1*s*. a year to the lord of the manor, and eked out an existence as smallholders, the family income being supplemented by a little day labour. As commons were inclosed in the late 18th and 19th centuries the number of squatters declined, to the satisfaction of improving landlords and churchmen who saw the lifestyle as one producing immorality, idleness, and dishonesty. At Aston-on-Clun, for instance, the initiative *c*. 1804 to inclose the 160-a. common came from the new rector of Hopesay, whose principal concern was to see the immoral commons dwellers cleared off.

As late as the 1860s village cottages were frequently tumbledown, leaky, and insanitary. One-bedroom cottages were common in many parts of the county and were a great source of pauperism, immorality, incest, and illegitimacy. On some estates the cottages were a 'disgrace to a civilized country', and were not even cheap: for 'miserable' dwellings in Loppington the larger landowners charged £3 10*s*. a year, the smaller proprietors £4 or £5. Elsewhere landowners were demolishing (but not replacing) cottages to escape the reproach of owning them. At Lydham, Lea, and Oakley many cottages were demolished in the 1790s, and in the 1860s many labourers had to live in Bishop's Castle and walk to and from their work. They endured the dual disadvantage of living in an urban slum and earning only a low agricultural wage.

A few Shropshire landlords did try to improve labourers' houses, although they knew they would never get a worthwhile return on their investment. Lord Craven, for instance, built two-bedroomed cottages at Stokesay, while Sir Rowland Hill (2nd Viscount Hill, 1842), who owned 300-400 north Shropshire cottages, was reputed a cottage improver. Other landlords assisted the local poor by leasing them small allotments of land. Thus in the mid 19th century Sir Baldwin Leighton was moving tenants from cabins on Wattlesborough heath into model cottages along the Shrewsbury-Welshpool turnpike road and was renting the prudent ones, with savings, an acre or two on which a cow could be kept. Such landlords were, however, very much in the minority. Some were dissuaded from trying to improve the labourers' standard of living in this way by the almost universal disapproval of farmers, who objected that cottagers with allotments made unreliable labourers, especially in the busy seasons, as they preferred to work their own plots rather than take paid employment.

As the 19th century progressed rural wages and conditions remained depressed, and even the most industrious labourer faced a miserable old age

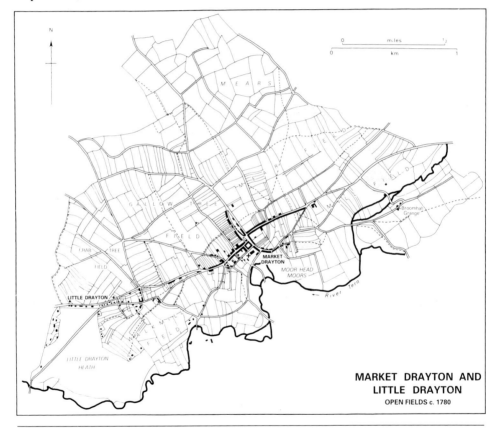

MARKET DRAYTON AND LITTLE DRAYTON

OPEN FIELDS c. 1780

The open fields around Market Drayton survived well into the 19th century, and vestiges of them can be seen even today, fossilized in curving property boundaries. Presumably the main obstacle to inclosure was the complexity of the landholding arrangements.

in the workhouse. Those who pressed for improvements risked getting known as troublemakers or political agitators and evicted. Given such poverty, people increasingly drifted away from the countryside to the industrial and urban areas in search of a better life. From the poorest areas the drift became an exodus, and in the 1880s the population of the Clun area fell by 23 per cent.

Inclosure

The late 18th and 19th century saw the final inclosure of the county's remaining open fields and most of its common wastes. Despite the long tradition of inclosure in Shropshire perhaps twelve per cent of the county's

DRY-STONE WALL ON WESTON HILL
In 1810 some 800 a. of uplands in Weston Rhyn, Dudleston, and Ifton Rhyn, north of Oswestry, were inclosed. Poorly built stone walls were constructed from stones cleared off the new fields. Across the valley lies Selattyn, whose uplands were also largely inclosed in this period.

area still survived to be improved in this way, whether by parliamentary Act or by private agreement. In a few places open fields survived into the period, not to be inclosed until the 18th or even 19th century. That seems to have been especially so around towns, presumably because the number of people with holdings complicated the process. Bridgnorth, Ludlow, and Shifnal all still had open field strips around them in the 18th century, as did Market Drayton, whose remarkably extensive open fields were mapped in 1787. Principally, however, it was common wastes that remained to be inclosed during the period. Between 1760 and 1820 there was over three times as much inclosure in north Shropshire as in the south, landowners being attracted by the great potential fertility of the heavy clay soils and peat mosses despite the large investment that might be required in drainage costs. One of the biggest projects was the drainage and division into fields under an Act of 1777 of Baggy Moor in the Perry valley, formerly under water each winter. In the early 19th century, as war and dearth forced up grain prices, the less fertile but more easily tackled heathlands of the north were dealt with. By 1820 north Shropshire landowners had inclosed more than 20,000 acres by Act, and there were few commons left. The old open heathlands had been replaced by a planned landscape of almost grid-like regularity, of large rectangular hedged fields, of wide and straight roads, and of newly built farmhouses, which lay isolated amongst their fields rather than in the old villages. During the rest of the 19th century almost all parliamentary inclosure was confined to the extensive hills of the south-west and south-east where, earlier, inclosure must have seemed unprofitable.

By the 1840s, when nearly 11,000 acres were inclosed by parliamentary means, the potential for profit was clear. Good land inclosed from Clun forest increased in annual value from 2*s*. or 3*s*. an acre when it was open sheep pasture to 10*s*. or 12*s*. when inclosed. Most newly inclosed land became permanent pasture, but some, even in hilly districts, was capable of growing grain or of conversion to meadow. Good grain, for instance, was grown *c*. 1800 on parts of the Long Mynd inclosed in 1790, and even before inclosure was completed wild land on the slopes of hills in Clun forest was being converted to water meadows. As today, improvement raised some regrets. The agricultural writer Joseph Plymley noted that 'a great deal of beauty' was often spoiled by inclosure: Clun forest, for instance, in its uninclosed state, was 'a fine specimen of smooth and extended turf, with every variation of swelling banks and retired dingles'. Other landowners planted up all or part of their allotted inclosures with trees. Opponents' dislike of plantations was exacerbated by the fact that it was usually foreign conifers, rather than English hardwoods that were grown. The poet Wordsworth scathingly called such plantations 'vegetable manufactories'. The more prevalent view in the utilitarian 1840s, however, was probably that of Francis Marston, involved as surveyor in 19 or 20 Shropshire inclosures. His opinion was that inclosure and plantation made the land more useful and no less fair, and he considered that the side of Clunbury Hill and the whole top of the Long Mynd should be planted to increase their utility and beauty and at the same time to improve the local climate.

PLOUGHING IN 1813
Ploughing with swing ploughs on the earl of Bradford's estate, painted by Thomas Weaver. The smock, or 'slop-frock', sometimes soaked in linseed oil to give a degree of protection from rain, remained the usual garb of farmworkers for another 50 or 60 years.

Improvements in arable farming

Although as late as the 1850s and 1860s oxen were still occasionally to be found at work in the county, they were generally replaced in Shropshire in the decades either side of 1800 by the more intelligent and versatile horse. Little systematic work-horse breeding went on, however, and stock with any claim to a recognized pedigree remained rare until the late 19th century. Thus when Thomas Whitmore's effects were valued at Apley in 1795 wagon horses – Derby, Poppit, Tolley, Captain, Smiler, Whitefoot, Lion, and Short were described by age, colour, and condition. The most valuable at £27 6s. was Captain, a 'black horse 9 years old'. Least valuable, at £5 5s, was Short, an old black broken-winded horse. From then until the popularization of the tractor in the 20th century most ploughing in Shropshire was done by horse. Companies were set up in the 1860s at Whitchurch, Market Drayton, and Shrewsbury which offered contract steam ploughing, but the county's fields were not suited to the large steam engines and the Shrewsbury company collapsed only four years after its foundation.

By the later 18th century Shropshire farmers were following a sort of 'alternate husbandry', a more scientific form of arable cultivation which had been in use in eastern England from the late 17th century. The classic 'Norfolk' rotation was of four courses: a well-manured turnip crop prepared the soil for the following season's barley, after which a one year clover ley restored nitrogen to the ground for use by the next year's wheat. Thus the soil was kept in good heart, valuable fodder provided for livestock, and fallowing eliminated. In Shropshire rotations were often longer, of six or seven years, and many farmers retained fallows, but from the 1780s the increasing amounts of rye grass, clover, and turnip seed advertised at farm sales bear witness to the spread of alternate husbandry. Pea and potato cultivation also increased. Peas, like turnips, could be weeded by hoe, and they conferred the nitrogen-fixing benefits of the clover ley. Potatoes, increasingly popular for both animal and human consumption, could be grown on soils too heavy for turnips. Within a generation the adaptable swede and the hardier mangold-wurzel provided alternatives to the turnip, and other fodder crops such as cabbages and vetches were being tried.

From the 1840s advances in agricultural science and improved sea transport gave alternatives to traditional fertilizers and dressings such as manure, night soil, soot, lime, and marl. From Peru and Africa came guano (largely bird droppings), from Chile nitrates, from Germany potash, and from other parts of Britain superphosphates and basic slag.

The full benefit of these often expensive manures was only realized when land was properly drained. From the late 18th century Shropshire's 'gentlemen' and 'best' farmers had been underdraining their land, but it was expensive and the timber- or stone-filled drains were liable to clog or collapse. A new era of underdraining began in the 1840s with the invention of a machine that made cheap cyclindrical clay pipes, and the introduction of government loans for drainage projects. By the 1850s tile and pipe drains were to be found beneath much of the county's cultivated land.

Increasingly from the 1850s the seeds sown in the enriched and better-

THRESHING CONTRACTORS, ABOUT 1920
Threshing contractors on a Shropshire farm, probably about 1920. The steam engine pulls the threshing box, to which is attached an automatic trusser, a precursor of the baler. Behind a man thatches a rick to keep it dry.

drained soil were identified by name, enabling the discerning farmer to select the strain best suited to his land. Yields rose, and although it is difficult to generalize, tenfold yields of wheat and barley were common in the late 18th century but fifteenfold ones in the 1850s.

The period was also one of marked improvements in farm equipment. Iron rollers and harrows appeared in the 1780s, although it was not until the 1840s and 1850s that Shropshire farmers generally began to replace their wooden ploughs with iron ones. Around 1800 horse-driven winnowing and threshing machines began to appear. At first threshers were probably fixed installations in farm buildings, but portable ones were soon developed and

A PRIZE RAM
One of a pair owned by a Mr. Billings and painted by Thomas Weaver at Shrewsbury in 1824. It may be a New Leicester, but the distortions introduced by the artist to emphasize the size of the animal's body make it difficult to be sure.

with them threshing contractors. Other machinery too first appeared at that time, much – like chaff and turnip cutters and grain mills – associated with stock feeding. All such machines remained horse- or hand-driven until the 1860s, when portable steam engines began to spread quickly.

Machines enabling row cultivation, namely seed drills and horse hoes, took longer to evolve and be accepted than other innovations. Eighteenth-century inventors like Jethro Tull tried hard to convince farmers of the superiority of row cultivation over the broadcasting of seed by hand, both in terms of the economical use of seed and in the improved efficiency of weeding and harvesting which row cultivation allowed, but it was only in the earlier 19th century that seed drills began to be used in Shropshire.

The last big farming operation to be mechanized was harvesting. It was the most labour-intensive of all. In early 19th-century Shropshire wheat was still reaped with broad hooks or sickles, while barley, oats, and hay were mown with scythes. In the 1840s tedding machines appeared which turned the cut hay, and slightly later horse hay rakes, and together they greatly lessened farmers' worries about getting in the hay crop. In the 1850s American horse-drawn reapers and reaper-mowers quickly gained popularity among larger farmers, although on small farms corn and hay continued to be cut by hand for another 100 years.

Many of the new machines appearing on Shropshire farms in the late 18th and 19th centuries came from far afield, even America. There were, however, some local manufacturers including Thomas Corbett, who in 1868 built the Perseverance Ironworks in Castle Foregate, Shrewsbury, the largest works of its type in the west midlands. Corbett's ploughs, horse hoes, drills, and rollers were known internationally by the 1870s. Other successful implement manufacturers in Shropshire included Gowers and Rodenhursts, both of Market Drayton, the Smiths of Whitchurch, and the Dorsetts of Madeley.

Livestock husbandry

On a few farms some of the old Shropshire types of cattle such as the dark red Bishop's Castle breed and the Montgomeryshire Smokey Faced breed could still be found in the mid 19th century. By then, however, the county's farmers had been improving the native longhorned stock for some 50 years by the use of bulls from Cheshire, Lancashire, and the east midlands. Further breed improvements followed. The Hereford's characteristics were standardized in the early 19th century, and its ability to mature early and on poor conditions made it a popular beef animal in south Shropshire. Nevertheless both the Hereford and the improved Longhorn were poor milk producers, and Holderness, Leicestershire, Ayrshire, and Alderney (or Channel Islands) breeds were tried in Shropshire. By and large, however, Longhorns remained the main Shropshire dairy animal until improved Shorthorns began to be bred in the county in the 1830s and 1840s by gentlemen farmers like Lord Hill. Shorthorns soon became popular, and

CATTLE AT BUILDWAS ABBEY, 1841
The improvers of the Hereford breed were proud of their achievement. This picture, painted by James Pardon, probably shows Thomas Jones, the tenant farmer at Buildwas, showing his stock to his landlord, Walter Moseley. The cowman wears the distinctive regional smock with its large, heavy collar.

between about 1875 and the 1950s, when they were overtaken by the larger and higher yielding Friesians, they were the commonest dairy cow in Shropshire.

In sheep farming too new strains were entering the county by 1800, although the old Shropshire sheep was still widely found on the uplands and commons of south Shropshire. Landowners played a part in improving the available stock but the most notable sheep breeders were tenant farmers like George Adney of Harley and Samuel Meire of Berrington. Diffusion of the Dorset breed, for instance, said to produce excellent stock when crossed with the old Shropshire, was greatly assisted by the sale of 700 Dorset and Wiltshire sheep from the Atcham estate in 1789. Similarly the appearance in Shropshire of the nationally respected New Leicester and Southdown breeds in the 20 years after 1800 was largely through their acquisition by gentlemen farmers. By 1853 a recognized Shropshire breed had evolved from cross breeding and was being chosen by many of the county's farmers in preference to Leicesters and Southdowns, whose numbers declined from the 1840s.

In the later 18th century the Shropshire pig was widely found in western England. Reputedly the largest British pig, it was white, with drop ears, a coarse, wiry coat, and a long body. By 1800 that type was being improved by a cross with the Berkshire breed to produce a spotted type, said to fatten more quickly to about 28 stone, reached in two years. Berkshire cross sows usually produced litters of seven twice a year. Berkshires maintained their popularity in the county throughout the 19th century, and few of the other improving breeds, such as Chinese or Neapolitan, were found.

1875-1985

The Great Depression: 1875-1914

Hard times arrived for farmers in the 1870s as prices, especially of cereals, began to collapse. Many blamed successive years of bad weather, but more important was the increasing quantity of cheap grain imported from North America, Australia, and New Zealand.

As the depression stretched into the 1880s and 1890s landed proprietors had to take more responsibility for their estates. Many reduced farm rents by 15 or 20 per cent, and assisted their tenants by financing drainage schemes and other permanent improvements. The great estates provided valuable stability in a period of uncertainty and Shropshire, with over half its area belonging to estates of 3,000 a. or more, was fortunate in that respect.

Eventually that stability was undermined by the continuing depression and the steady decline in rents. As late as 1894 the *Shrewsbury Chronicle* asserted (untruly) that 'such a thing as a Shropshire estate offered for sale is an absolute novelty'. But the next year saw the first indications of what was to follow, with the sale of the 4,000-a. Condover estate and the beginning of the break-up of the 16,500-a. Hawkstone estate. By 1901 Lord Powis had sold *c.* 6,000 a. in the county and in 1912, made nervous by Lloyd George's 1910 Finance Act, he offered the 5,800-a. Montford estate for sale. Also offered for sale in 1912 were 8,600 a. of the duke of Sutherland's Lilleshall estate, most being sold to sitting tenants. The remainder of the Lilleshall estate was sold in 1914 and 1917.

One of the ways in which the Victorian landlord expressed his interest in local farming was by his patronage of local agricultural societies. The most important in Shropshire were the Chamber of Agriculture (founded 1866) and the Shropshire and West Midlands Agricultural Society (started 1875), and in the 1880s Lord Powis attended meetings of the former and was president of the latter. Another aristocrat interested in farmers' problems was the 4th duke of Sutherland, and in 1904 he helped to found the Newport & District Agricultural Co-operative Trading Society Ltd., whose purpose was to obtain the advantages of bulk purchase and transport for the small producer.

Farmers too began to band together, and in 1908 those of the Shrewsbury district formed an association in the face of demands from butchers that they should guarantee fatstock free from disease. Similar associations were also formed in 1908 at Wellington, Oswestry, and Craven Arms, and they were among the earliest branches to join the new National Farmers' Union later that year. At first, however, recruitment to the N.F.U. was slow, and in 1914 county membership was still under 500.

In the 1870s, as for the next century, Shropshire's main cereal growing area was the centre and east of the county. To some extent Shropshire's cereal farmers were cushioned from the worst effects of the depression because they grew mainly barley, whose price fell considerably less than that of wheat, which plummeted by half in the years after 1875. In the 1870s most Shropshire arable farmers on light land followed a four- or five-course rotation involving roots, spring-sown barley, clover (left for two years in the five-course rotation), and wheat. Those with strong or heavy land followed a different pattern, generally fallow, wheat, clover, barley, fallow, wheat, and peas or beans, although commercial pressures led to less use of fallows in the 1880s and 1890s.

A PRIZE PIG
William Gwynn's picture of a prize pig owned by Sir C. W. Rouse-Boughton, Bt. (d. 1821), of Downton Hall near Ludlow. The pig, a Shropshire-Berkshire cross, was 20 months old and weighed 33 score 15 lb., or just over 6 cwt.

Livestock rearing was heavily concentrated in the uplands south-west of the Severn and in north-west Shropshire. That had long been so, although the steep fall in wheat prices in the 1870s had also led to the grassing down of land in the Clee Hills that had previously been the county's most important wheat growing area. The usual practice was to raise store cattle on the lower slopes, although yard feeding increased in the years before 1914. While Herefords were most common, Welsh, Lancashire, Longhorns, Shorthorns, Ayrshires, and Devons were all still found. On the upper slopes

A LATE VICTORIAN FARM SALE
An audience of well dressed farmers appreciatively eye a fat Hereford-type bull being offered for sale by the Craven Arms auctioneers Jackson & McCartney. The picture was probably taken on a farm near Craven Arms in the late 19th century.

Clun forest or Kerry Hill sheep were run. Shropshire sheep were confined mainly to the arable lowlands, where they were often folded on root crops such as mangolds. That branch of sheep rearing declined during the depression as the cold, wet weather brought sheep rot, root crops were hit by fly infestations, and mutton and wool prices fell as imports flooded into the country.

Horse breeding was revived. In the early 19th century 'the Shropshire type' of fine quality hunter had been a noted regional breed, but horse breeding in the county had declined by the 1880s. The demand for work horses from farmers, brewers, and carters remained strong throughout the period and in the early 1880s societies were formed at Shrewsbury, Ellesmere, and Ludlow to encourage their breeding. Gradually, however, some of the county's old horse fairs, such as Ludlow and Oswestry, declined, and in the 1920s the only substantial centres for horse sales were Shrewsbury and Craven Arms.

On the heavier soils of the north of the county dairy farming predominated. The absence of suitable rail links greatly limited the amount of milk that was distributed to neighbouring towns, and most was used to make butter and Cheshire cheese in farmhouse dairies. Some cheese was sold to travelling dealers, and there were also several large cheese fairs where it could be disposed of, such as Ellesmere, Market Drayton, Shrewsbury, Wem, and Whitchurch.

The numbers engaged in agriculture declined considerably between 1870 and 1914, labourers by 36 per cent. The causes were several but included the introduction of compulsory elementary education in the 1870s which removed cheap juvenile labour, and low wages which led men to seek jobs in towns and industry. Average weekly wages rose from 12s. 3d. in 1867-70, to 17s. 5d. by 1898, and to £1 7s. in 1918 when labour was scarce. That was for a 59-hour week in summer and a 52-hour one in winter, both excluding meal breaks.

As wage rates fluctuated so did workers' interest in trade unions. The North Herefordshire and South Shropshire Agricultural Labourers' Mutual Improvement Society was formed in 1871. Its slogan was 'Emigration, Migration, but not Strikes', and it sent surplus labour from low wage areas to better paid employment in northern England. But despite this pioneering venture Shropshire's part in the early history of conventional agricultural trade unionism was small, and in 1872 when the inaugural meeting of the first national union of farm workers was held at Leamington the county's

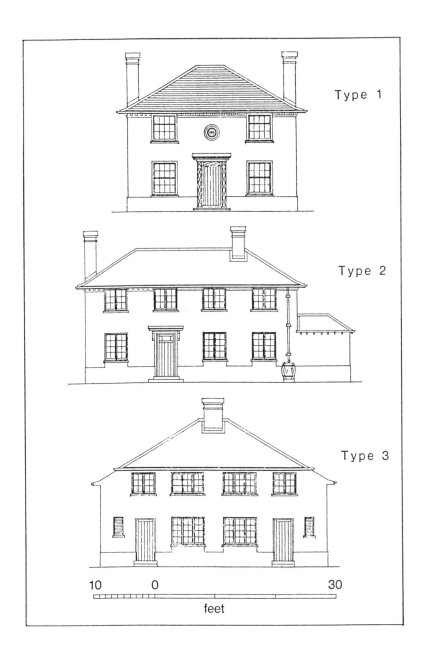

Type 1

Type 2

Type 3

10   0   30

feet

64

representative was Sir Baldwyn Leighton, a sympathetic landowner.

From the later 19th century the county council had the power to provide smallholdings, but it did not act upon it. Only from 1907, when parliament made such provision compulsory, did the council begin to buy (or occasionally lease) farms to subdivide into smallholdings, intended to provide an opening into farming for suitable applicants. By 1914 it had provided 93 smallholdings covering 2,064 a., mainly in the north. Apparently to the council's surprise the scheme proved profitable. After 1918 a further 3,500 a. were purchased to provide a start in farming for ex-servicemen, and another 3,500 a. were bought in the late 1920s and 1930s. Most smallholders concentrated on dairying, achieving high stocking rates with silage making, heavy fertilizer applications, and the buying in of winter feed. Where necessary new houses and agricultural buildings of nationally approved types were built for the smallholders, and to this day they remain a distinctive feature of the Shropshire landscape.

Slump: 1914-1939

The First World War brought a brief period of prosperity for farmers as the government encouraged home production, especially of grain, in order to reduce the amount of scarce shipping space devoted to foodstuffs. The need to raise home production became acute as U-boat attacks continued to sink much merchant shipping heading for Britain, and in April 1917 only six weeks' supply of wheat remained in the country. From 1920, however, imports again pushed down the price of home-grown produce, and those farmers old enough to remember regarded the years between the wars as an era of depression even more severe than that before 1914.

SMALLHOLDERS' HOUSES, 1919
At the end of the First World War the government required borough and district councils to begin to provide better quality housing for the working classes – council houses. County councils also began to buy up farm land, to be split into smallholdings for rent, to give men a start in farming. Houses of various nationally approved types were built, according to the size of the smallholdings. Houses of these 1919 designs can be seen on county council smallholdings all over Shropshire, for instance at Emstrey, near Shrewsbury.

The great landowners continued to dispose of their estates, taking advantage of a buoyant real estate market after a generation of low land values and farmers' unwillingness to pay true economic rents. In Shropshire probably over 80,000 a. were offered for sale between 1918 and 1923 when the pace of sales was slackening. In some cases whole estates were sold, as in 1919 when H. D. Corbet ended almost 400 years of family ownership by putting the 8,000-a. Sundorne Castle estate on the market. Elsewhere land-owners rationalized their estates by disposing of outlying portions; in 1918 Lord Forester sold his Dothill estate, near Wellington, and Lord Acton outlying parts of the Aldenham estate. Often farms were sold to sitting tenants, and the larger part of the lands disposed of by Lord Barnard, Lord Bath, and Lord Brownlow was acquired by their tenants. In the county as a whole the percentage of farmland in owner-occupancy rose from 8 per cent

THRESHING AT ELCOTT FARM, NEEN SAVAGE
An early 20th-century photograph showing farm labourers loading unthreshed corn into the threshing box. This is powered by a belt drive off the steam engine. The work was both dirty and dangerous. On the right a neat thatched rick can be seen.

in 1911, to 18 per cent in 1922, and to 30 per cent by 1941.

Many farmers, however, viewed the prospect of becoming owner-occupiers with disquiet, and in 1919 the county branch of the N.F.U. spoke of farmers being saddled with farms for the rest of their lives at figures far beyond their true commercial value. As the price of foodstuffs fell from April 1920 farmers were frantic not to lose the protective shield of those owners that remained. Tenants on Sir Beville Stanier's 4,000-a. Peplow estate asked if there was anything they could do to avert the catastrophe that threatened with his contemplated sale of the Hall and estate. Stanier, while expressing concern for his tenants' welfare, said he had no alternative but to

CLEANING PARSNIPS NEAR EDGMOND
A scene from the 1930s. Farm work was ill paid, hard, and in this case cold and monotonous.

move to a smaller house and less expensive surroundings.

As the great estates were broken up the fabric of the countryside deteriorated. Of about 90 country houses standing in the 1870s there was no trace of at least 35 in 1952. More generally the depressed state of farm incomes meant that buildings, hedges, drainage schemes and the standard of cultivation as a whole often declined between the wars. Only a small part of the deterioration was countered by the county council's increasing work on rivers and land drainage and by its campaigns against injurious weeds and vermin like the musk rat.

One way in which farmers reacted in the face of economic difficulties was by forming private co-operatives. One of the earliest, formed in 1866, was the Wem Cow Club, which had 68 members in 1913. In 1929 there were seven co-operatives based in the county, ranging from the Market Drayton & District Agricultural and Small Holding Society, with 43 members and £13 worth of sales, to the Shrewsbury-based Shropshire Farmers with 1,226 members and £99,655 of sales. Other groups included the Llangedwyn Farmers' Co-operative Cheese Association, Oswestry, which manufactured dairy products, and the Burwarton Poultry Society marketing eggs and poultry.

During the difficult years between the wars N.F.U. membership grew slowly, from a paid-up membership of 2,225 in 1920 to over 3,500 by 1945. One of its main campaigns, in the 1920s, was in favour of cutting county council expenditure, and N.F.U. candidates were elected to the council to that end. Farms were de-rated in 1930, and N.F.U. interest in council business soon waned. As the N.F.U. became more powerful, and landowners came to be represented by the Country Landowners' Association, the Chamber of Agriculture declined in importance. In 1932 it had 271 members, and though it still lobbied parliament on agricultural matters, thenceforward it devoted more effort to organizing educational and social activities. It still had about 200 members in the late 1970s when it was revivified.

Farm work remained an unattractive proposition between the wars, and parents often encouraged their sons to seek alternative, usually urban, employment. Although in 1918 the working week was reduced to 50 hours in the summer and 48 in the winter it rose again on many farms after 1921 to 54 as prices fell once more. Wages were also lowered, from a post-war record of 46s. a week to as low as 30s., and they remained at about that level until the Second World War.

About the only benefit enjoyed by farm workers was cheap housing, and in 1939 cottage rents were about 3*s*. a week compared with 6*s*. to 10*s*. for urban accommodation. Otherwise the standard of living was poor, especially where there were dependent children at home. Most of the weekly wage went on food and rent. Clothes had to be paid for by the man's harvest earnings and, when available, potato and beet lifting by the wife. Cottages were sparsely furnished and social life was limited by lack of time and money. Most men visited the pub only rarely, and the most popular entertainment was the wireless, often bought on hire purchase.

The renewed depression also hit membership of the National Union of Agricultural Workers, which in 1918, although only established for five years in the county, had over 70 branches and a subscription income of £1,600. By 1931 however, there were just over 40 branches and income had fallen to under £1,000.

During the First World War the government encouraged cereal growing, but generally the trend was downward, especially with the end of government subsidies in 1920, and the acreage growing cereals fell from 173,000 in the 1870s to just under 76,000 in the 1930s. Rotations were lengthened from four to five courses, which produced a higher output of cash crops in the form of potatoes and beet.

After 1918 the traditional root crops – turnips, swedes, and mangolds – were grown less and less as the numbers of folded sheep fell and the winter feeding of cattle in yards, increasingly popular before 1914, became unprofitable. That decline was partly offset by an increase in the acreage of sugar beet, first grown in 1922, whose popularity was boosted by the introduction of a government subsidy in 1925 and by the opening of the Allscott sugar factory in 1927. In 1934 16,017 a. in the county grew beet, and the Allscott factory dealt with 177,592 tons. In 1965 the figure was 249,225 tons. In 1987 405 growers serving Allscott grew about 8,800 ha. (21,745 a.) of beet a year.

After 1918 there was also a limited tendency to replace root crops with vegetables for human consumption. Near Whixall, for instance, early vegetables were produced both for local markets and for ones as far away as Liverpool. Small undertakings with cultivation under glass were started in all parts of the county. At Roden the Co-operative Wholesale Society opened a small factory for jam and bottled fruits before 1914, and practically the whole village became involved in the venture. Otherwise little fruit was grown commercially in the county apart from in the extreme south-east where cider apples, cherries, and damsons continued to be cultivated.

Cattle and sheep fattening remained the complementary, indeed at times dominant, activity on arable farms in the central and eastern districts. Irish Shorthorns and Herefords were the most popular cattle, fed either on pasture (from April or May) or in yards. With winter yard feeding the tendency was for the old fashioned rations based on roots, hay, or straw to give way to feeding on beet pulp, available from the Allscott sugar factory. That was mostly blended with molasses and fed with concentrates and a reduced amount of hay to provide a balanced ration. Dairy cattle too were fed in that way. In the 1920s and 1930s sheep, mainly Cluns and Kerry Hills, were increasingly folded on beet tops rather than on roots, and by 1948 close folding on roots was 'something of a spectacle' and open folding on beet tops and catch crops was general.

In those years more emphasis was placed on feeding the livestock than the land, and yields from both temporary and permanent grass fell in the 1920s and 1930s. Part of the trouble lay in the decline of liming after 1900. In the 1880s up to three tons an acre were applied to acid soils in the Ludlow and Much Wenlock areas every eight years. In the early 20th century, however, farmers came to believe, erroneously, that chemical fertilizers made lime unnecessary and the practice dropped off. When, in the 1930s, farmers began to realize that liming was necessary, they found that application of the necessary amounts could be expensive and time consuming. On a farm at Bromfield it took one man a whole winter to apply sufficient burnt lime and slag, up to 55 cwt. an acre.

Liquid milk sales rose considerably between the wars. As roads improved farmers could get their milk to railway stations and thence to Birmingham and even London, and to new rural factories making cream, butter, and cheese. A creamery opened at Minsterley in 1909, and in 1932 was one of the first to make tinned cream. Other establishments included the Wem milk depot, which concentrated on making Cheshire cheese, the Crudgington creamery, and factories at Ellesmere and Whittington. Cadburys became one of the largest purchasers of milk in north-east Shropshire after its Knighton (Staffs.) factory opened in 1911, and the firm had another milk factory at Stoke on Tern 1935-8.

The establishment of the Milk Marketing Board with a nationally agreed year-round guaranteed price for milk in 1933 led to a steadier year-round output of milk and cheese. Previously there had been heavy reliance on summer milk production, pigs being fed on the inevitable surplus of whey.

Pigs continued to be kept on many dairy farms until 1939, but by then they were fed on mash and dry feed.

The growth of the liquid milk market and of commercial creameries threatened farmhouse cheese making. In fact it survived until the Second World War, largely because the farmer's family provided cheap labour. In 1915 a quarter of all Cheshire cheese was made in Shropshire, and in the 1920s Shropshire was one of the four largest cheese producing counties in England. At Whitchurch cheese fair an annual average of 1,411 tons of cheese was sold between 1925 and 1929.

SHROPSHIRE'S FIRST TRACTOR
Interestingly, the first owner of a tractor driven by the internal combustion engine was not one of Shropshire's great landowners but a tenant. This photo shows Thomas Dale Powell bringing a load of hay to his farm at Moreton Corbet, probably during the First World War. Powell (d.1935) was also an early car owner, and was active in the N.F.U., the West Midlands Agricultural Society, and the Wem and District Agricultural Association.

In 1939-45 the country's farmers were again called on greatly to increase production to feed a wartime population. The government imported tractors and other machinery from America, and by 1945 Britain's farmers were the most highly mechanized in the world and were producing record-breaking harvests. Many farmers feared that peace would bring the withdrawal of government support and hard times once more, but new government policies after 1945 guaranteed prices and markets for basic products such as

THREE SHROPSHIRE YEARLING RAMS
These fine rams were bred by Mr. J. W. Lockhart (on right), a Culmington farmer, in the 1920s. The woolly face was demanded by the international market, but it led to eye infections and was later bred out. In recent years there has been a happy revival of interest in the Shropshire breed, and it is no longer the rarity it had become.

fat stock, milk, eggs, cereals, potatoes, and sugar beet, and gave tenant farmers greater security on their holdings. With that support production and yields rose markedly, and in 1972 Britain grew 60 per cent of the food it consumed compared with 30 per cent in 1938. In 1973 Britain joined the E.E.C., or Common Market; its farmers still had price guarantees but faced increased competition from continental farmers.

After 1945 there were further sales of the great estates. In 1947 Lord Acton sold the 930-a. Aldenham estate to his father-in-law and went to farm in Southern Rhodesia, not the only Shropshire landowner to seek opportunities and traditional values outside post-war Britain. In 1954 Ronald Knox noted dryly that Southern Rhodesia 'seemed to be peopled entirely with Shropshire county families and Central European refugees'. In the 1950s Lord Brownlow sold the remaining 2,000 a. of the Bridgwater estate, and in the 1950s and 1960s Lord Barnard disposed of land at Cressage and Harley. Nevertheless in the 1980s about a dozen of the great estates survived, among them those of Lords Bradford, Forester, Harlech, and Plymouth. Increasingly as farms fell vacant estates took them in hand and managed them directly.

By 1979 average farm size had more than doubled since the 1930s to about 120 a. and farms of over 300 a. (120 ha.) were increasing in number, comprising 10 per cent of all farms. As in the 19th century the largest farms were among the sheep walks of central and south-eastern Shropshire, and the smallest in the dairying districts of the north. After 1945 owner-occupation increased, and by 1979 65 per cent of Shropshire's farms were wholly or mainly owned by their occupiers.

After the war the N.F.U. and farmers' co-operatives became better organized. County N.F.U. membership rose to 6,000 by 1958. The county executive in Shrewsbury took responsibility for presenting a general voice on common issues, sometimes a difficult task given the division between the arable and dairying north and the mainly livestock interests of the south, and also the greater militancy of northern farmers. Co-operatives that survived the war expanded into general trading companies, supplying a broad range of agricultural goods at a discount. South Shropshire Farmers, founded in 1917, had a turnover of £11 million by 1979. Another big organization, with sales of £3.5 million in 1977, was Wrekin Farmers, which provided members with grain drying and storage facilities and supplied fertilizers and feedstuffs.

From 1949 the numbers of farm workers fell steadily, in Shropshire by 40 per cent in the 16 years to 1965. After the war the working week gradually shortened and wages rose, and in the 1970s and 1980s farm workers were better off in real terms than ever before. Nevertheless farm work remained one of the most poorly paid forms of skilled work. Like the N.F.U., the Agricultural Workers' Union gradually became larger, stronger, and better organized; it had 85 branches in Shropshire in 1946, 120 in 1958, their main local concerns being recovering arrears of wages and obtaining damages for members injured at work.

One factor which reduced the number of farm workers was the introduction of more efficient machinery. Tractors driven by internal

FOOT AND MOUTH PRECAUTIONS 1967
A press photo taken on 26 October, the day after the foot and mouth disease outbreak was confirmed at Bryn farm, Nantmawr. The cheerful faces belie the fact that the bulldozer had come to bury more than 250 animals. Sadly, it was a scene that was to become all too familiar over the next year.

combustion engines first appeared in the 1890s, but it was not until 1917, when the U-boat blockade caused the government to order 5,000 American 'Fordson' tractors to help with the ploughing up campaign, that they began to gain popularity. In the 1920s and 1930s improvements such as three-point linkages and pneumatic tyres were made, and by 1942 there were 1,949 tractors in the county. The ploughing up campaign of 1939-45 spread the tractor's use; there were 3,362 in Shropshire by 1944, and 6,597 by 1952. Combine harvesters (which combine all the jobs associated with cutting and threshing in one machine) had been used in America for many years before they were introduced to Britain in 1928; as with the tractor, it was only in the years after 1939 that they became a common sight in the countryside. Other machinery which rapidly found its way onto the county's farms after 1939 included the combine drill, potato planters and lifters, and sugar beet lifters.

Fertilizer use also increased. In the arable districts of east Shropshire, which had always used plenty of fertilizers, applications of nitrogen, phosphates, and potash rose by 31, 19, and 76 per cent respectively between 1944 and 1950. Similarly heavier stocking rates and higher milk yields in the 1950s were achieved by the liberal and efficient use of fertilizers. Farmers such as the Mayalls of Harmer Hill and Arthur Hollins of Fordhall farm, Market Drayton, who deliberately eschewed chemical fertilizers in favour of compost and dung to maintain soil fertility, were few and far between, and only in the 1980s did a demand really begin to appear for 'organic' farm produce.

In 1939, as war threatened, the government introduced a subsidy of £2 an acre to encourage farmers to plough up permanent grassland, as it was clear from the experience of 1914-18 that Britain would need rapidly to increase its food production. By April 1940 40,000 a. had been converted to arable in Shropshire, compared with 27,000 a. in 1917-18. In eastern Shropshire potatoes became a major crop, but generally most of the increased arable grew oats and mixed corn. The increased acreage of corn continued to be grown after the war as the government continued deficiency payments and introduced price guarantees, and in the 1970s the corn acreage of 193,000 was the highest in the county for at least a century.

In the main arable farming districts, around Newport, Wellington, Shifnal, and Bridgnorth, a few farmers gave up mixed farming and went over to rotations based on wheat, barley, potatoes, and sugar beet. Most farmers, however, preferred to retain the traditional emphasis on sheep and cattle feeding. Sheep were mainly Cluns crossed with Down rams; much of their winter was spent on beet tops and kale and the summer on rape and turnips. The fattening of beef cattle, mainly stores brought from south Shropshire, and plenty of Irish, remained essentially something that was done in stockyards over the winter.

In the animal rearing districts of south and west Shropshire the production of young store cattle remained important, although by the 1970s the poor prices made by small and late calves led to stores being kept longer and even in some cases retained for fattening. After the war sheep numbers rose in the upland districts as grant aid under the 1946 Hill Farming Act and the arrival of the crawler or caterpillar tractor allowed the conversion of scrub- and bracken-covered hills to pasture.

Between 1940 and 1947 pig numbers declined drastically as the government switched resources away from meat production to cereals and vegetables. Thereafter numbers increased and large, specialist pig farming units became common. The White breed became almost universal and the Old Spot largely disappeared. Poultry farms, both for eggs and meat, also became larger and more specialized after the war.

Between the 1930s and the 1980s the dairy industry prospered and developed. Mechanical rather than hand milking spread in the 1930s and 1940s, and by 1950 there were 2,600 milking machines in the county. Milk began to be collected by bulk tanker. Accredited herds – those certified as brucellosis-free – became more common, and Friesians increased in popularity to comprise 83 per cent of Shropshire's dairy cattle in 1965. As herds became larger and greater capital investment was needed for the new methods, many smaller dairy farmers sold up, and the number of registered milk producers in the county fell from 3,921 in 1963 to 1,460 in 1983. Farmhouse cheese making also declined after the war, although in the 1960s about 20 farmers around Market Drayton and Whitchurch still produced top-grade cheese. Dairy farmers were severely affected by the foot and mouth epidemic of 1967-8, which first appeared near Oswestry in October 1967. Only Cheshire suffered more, and the Ellesmere, Prees, and Wem areas were especially hard hit. The N.F.U. put the value of Shropshire animals lost at approximately £10 million: 65,722 cattle, 41,098 sheep, and 39,523 pigs. It took several years for the industry to recover properly, but generally milk production figures continued to climb ever upward, from 88 million gallons in 1963, to 100 million in 1973, and 125 million in 1983.

PRESENT AND FUTURE

By the early 1980s over-production was emerging as a problem in British farming; farmers had become too successful for their own good. Over the previous 35 years they had worked with successive governments whose policies had constantly encouraged expansion by exhortation and by more practical inducements such as grant aid, subsidies, and the funding of scientific research. Between the 1940s and 1981 milk yields rose from 2,355 litres per cow to 4,810, and wheat yields from 2.25 tonnes per hectare to 5.9. Increases only slightly less impressive were seen in other crops such as beet, potatoes, and turnips. In terms of national output, that of milk doubled between 1947 and the 1980s, wheat rose five times and barley six.

In fact, over-production was a European, and not a purely British, phenomenon, and the produce purchased and stored by the E.E.C. under its intervention schemes accumulated in ever larger butter and grain 'mountains' and milk and wine 'lakes'. By 1987 merely storing the surpluses cost £250 million a week. The situation attracted criticism on both financial and moral grounds, not least from the increasingly vociferous 'Green' lobby of environmental and related groups which expressed concern at the ecological cost of modern farming.

The reversal of past policies was heralded in 1984 by the announcement of milk production quotas; the news shocked dairy farmers, and many smaller ones were forced out of dairying and even farming altogether. Since then further quotas have been imposed and proposals have come from both Whitehall and Brussels to deal with other areas of over-production. Schemes have included price cuts (sometimes described as 'stabilisers'), subsidies for farmers to adopt recommended methods in sites of special scientific interest and environmentally sensitive areas, and incentives for diversification and forestry. In 1988 the government announced a 'set aside' scheme, under which farmers would be paid to take arable land out of production. Increasing emphasis was placed upon less intensive and chemical-dependent farming methods. Quality rather than quantity looked likely to become the watchword.

Diversification was also much discussed, and some schemes were being tried in practice. Redundant farm buildings were sold off for conversion to houses, or were renovated for use as farm shops. More and more farms were offering Bed and Breakfast. At Lynches farm, Yockleton, 'Butterfly World' opened in 1984, and by 1988 (renamed 'Country World') it was attracting thousands of visitors a year to see not only butterflies but also old livestock and poultry breeds and areas of conserved meadow. Flower and herb farming was being tried in several places, and by 1988 there were deer farms at Webscott farm near Myddle and at Walford College of Agriculture. Shropshire even had a snail farm!

However it is achieved it appears probable that over the next decade agricultural production will fall more closely into line with consumer demand than in the past. That correlation promises to be at an increasingly refined level as biotechnology develops plants and animals with specific qualities guaranteed. In stock breeding embryo transfer looks set to replace artificial insemination, while genetic engineering offers the possibility of the rapid development of greatly improved crop types far less reliant on chemicals for their high productivity levels and their disease and pest resistance. It is not the historian's task to offer predictions, but future commentators may see the last quarter of the 20th century as one of those crucial periods which saw farming suddenly and rapidly progress in new directions, and one in which the scientist came to be an equal partner with the farmer.